1961

MODERN GEOMETRY

Modern Geometry

AN INTEGRATED FIRST COURSE

Claire Fisher Adler

ASSOCIATE PROFESSOR OF MATHEMATICS
NEW YORK UNIVERSITY

McGRAW-HILL BOOK COMPANY, INC.

New York   Toronto   London

1958

MODERN GEOMETRY

Library of Congress Catalog Card Number 57-7992

v

00422

THE MAPLE PRESS COMPANY, YORK, PA.

PREFACE

The present text has been written for a beginning integrated, comprehensive, one-semester course in college geometry and is more suited to the needs of the present-day student than any of the existing texts. It takes into account two important factors: the mathematical background of the student and the time factor involved in his program. Both factors have been ignored far too long, as evidenced by the great number of advanced texts written beyond the grasp of large groups of people. Many students need knowledge of new developments for their future work, while others are eager to learn of the great discoveries that followed Euclid. If these discoveries are to be made more universally known, there must be a first course that bridges the great instructional gap existing between the completely synthetic Euclidean geometry of the secondary curriculum and abstract modern geometry with its emphasis on algebraic analysis. This book attempts to bridge that gap.

The text also takes cognizance of the time factor involved in the student's program. Because of already overcrowded schedules, students are under constant pressure to combine, compress, and condense their mathematical training. This means there is seldom time for more than one elective course in undergraduate geometry. As courses are now arranged, a single one-semester course will be a detailed exposition of some highly specialized theory. For instance, prospective teachers of the secondary curriculum frequently choose as an elective a course devoted exclusively to a study of advanced Euclidean geometry. Behind their selection lies the need, or desire, for a refresher course in the material they may be expected to teach later. But their goal is too limited. One of the crying needs of both secondary and college instruction is that the attainment of teachers be enlarged and their horizons widened. A single course in Euclidean geometry, however interesting it might be, is not a satisfactory background for

v

teachers who would guide, inspire, and properly orient the geometers of the future.   A sequence of courses would suffice for this purpose, but as just indicated, there is no time for prolonged undergraduate study.

The time factor has been considered by widening and extending the scope of the material offered in beginning courses.   Included and covered are elementary theory in foundations of geometry and basic theory in the fields of Euclidean, projective, and non-Euclidean geometry.   The separate theories are brought into one organic whole by means of certain unifying concepts.

Because of the wide scope of the material covered, much of interest has had to be omitted, while other topics have been condensed and summarized.   However, in cases where details are brief and proofs omitted, references are given to the literature in which complete treatments may be found.

A course such as the one for which the text is intended can be followed profitably by any advanced course dealing with some special development.   On the other hand, the course is of a terminal nature for those who have no time for further study in the field.

To provide for the varying backgrounds of readers, the text has been divided into three parts.   Part I is for persons with limited mathematical backgrounds including, of course, a knowledge of elementary Euclidean geometry.   Basic material to all that follows is found in Chaps. 1 and 2, dealing with foundations of the science and elementary logic.   Chapters 3, 4, and 5 concern advanced Euclidean geometry.   Its theory serves a dual purpose: it provides the refresher course desired by prospective teachers of the elementary curriculum, since proofs are based on elementary theorems; it also contains the roots or beginnings of projective geometry and thus shows how a new science is created.

In Part II, projective geometry is developed as a logical system of its own, quite independent of early Euclidean theory and quite independent of the distance concept.   This part is for the more mature and technically trained reader.   That the nonmetric projective theory is fascinating cannot be denied.   In addition its cultural and practical value for students of architecture, fine arts, and engineering has long been recognized.

In Chaps. 10 and 11 of Part II, the reader is introduced for the first time to the algebraic methods and techniques of modern geometers. These new tools are needed for the theories discussed in Part III. Prerequisites for the reading of these chapters are coordinate plane geometry and theory of equations.   In addition, considerable mathematical maturity is required.

Part III deals with metric geometries that result when the distance concept is added to the projective nonmetric theory of Part II. Chap. 12, the first in Part III, gives the historical background of these metric systems and their links with Euclid. The first metric projective system discussed is the one that so beautifully extends and generalizes Euclid. This material is recommended especially for prospective teachers who need perspective and background for their elementary teaching. The two metric systems discussed in the last two chapters will be recognized as the famous non-Euclidean geometries whose discovery was hailed as one of the greatest achievements of all times. Chapter 14 deals with hyperbolic non-Euclidean geometry, the first in order of discovery of these classical systems. Elliptic non-Euclidean geometry, which came later, is discussed in Chap. 15. In both chapters, models are used to introduce, illustrate, and make more realistic the strange new theories directly contradicting Euclid.

Early foundations of Euclidean geometry in Appendix A and Hilbert's famous axioms in Appendix B, together with an extensive bibliography in Appendix C, are inserted for the convenience of the reader.

For whatever of merit there is in the text, I am indebted to the following:

1. The distinguished scholars whose brilliant investigations are herewith presented in condensed form.

2. The members of the mathematics department of Washington Square College, New York University, and in particular, Professors Hollis Cooley, John Van Heijenoort, and Wilhelm Magnus. My special thanks are due Professor Magnus for his careful reading of a preliminary manuscript, which through various revisions has assumed the present form. It was from him that I learned of the results described in Sec. 2.9. This material is a contribution worthy of note and one that, to the best of my knowledge, cannot be found in any standard text.

It would be impossible to list individually all the suggestions and assistance contributed by others, including students and friends, but acknowledgment is herewith made of special services given by my sister Mrs. F. G. Danner, a student, Mr. Miles Galin, and a friend, Mrs. Lola Dorin.

Claire Fisher Adler

CONTENTS

PART THREE
NON-EUCLIDEAN AND METRIC PROJECTIVE GEOMETRIES

Part One

FOUNDATIONS AND SELECTED EUCLIDEAN GEOMETRY

Chapter 1

LOGICAL SYSTEMS AND
BASIC LAWS OF REASONING

Because of the vast amount of material now classified as geometry and because of the hundreds of years in which this material has been accumulating, it is impossible in discussing modern theories to do justice to all phases of the science. Yet, to specialize is to lose the perspective necessary for gaining a proper understanding of the nature, the scope, and the importance of geometry in the twentieth century. For this reason, it has been deemed advisable to consider first the underlying structure or foundation of geometry. Specialization will then come later.

Attention is focused first on logical systems, the pattern for which was set over 2,000 years ago when Euclid performed the amazing feat of collecting and organizing into a logical sequence practically all the existing facts about geometry. Euclid's geometry is but one example of a logical system. Algebra, which is based on axioms about the number system, is another example. Projective geometry and elementary non-Euclidean geometries are still other examples that are to be studied here.

In a logical system, a set of elements is given. Some of these elements are undefined, and certain facts or statements called axioms are assumed in connection with these undefined elements. The body of conclusions obtained by reasoning logically from these axioms and definitions represents the content of the system.

When a geometry is developed in this manner, it is called "axiomatic geometry," and the method employed is the "axiomatic method."

The axiomatic approach to a science has spread, like fire, throughout the whole of mathematics. In studying such an approach, one learns, perhaps in the most natural manner, of the far deeper problems which lie at the foundations of all mathematics.

Each of the basic topics, *undefined elements*, *axioms*, and *reasoning*, will now be considered in greater detail.

1.1 Undefined Elements and Axioms

The basic elements of a logical system are those in terms of which all the others are to be defined. *Point* and *line* are usually the undefined elements of elementary geometry, but there exist geometries in which the undefined elements are circles and spheres, or number pairs in a plane, or even other elements, depending upon the particular type of geometry to be studied.

To say that *point* and *line* are undefined elements may be puzzling, particularly since definitions for these terms can be found in any standard dictionary. However, a definition simply gives the meaning of one word in terms of others whose meaning is already clear. Simpler words may be defined in still more simple terms, and so on. Such a process would, therefore, lead to an endless regression if it were not agreed that certain basic words are to be left undefined.

For example, a line segment is, by definition, that portion of a line lying between two given points on the line. Here, *point* and *line* are undefined, as is also the word *between*.

Euclid defined a line as "length without breadth," and a straight line as a "line which lies evenly between two of its points." Here, the terms *length*, *breadth*, and *lies evenly* are all undefined; hence Euclid could just as well have used *line* as an undefined term.

Just as certain simple elements are chosen as fundamental ones, in terms of which all others are to be defined, so too some simple statements concerning the undefined elements are chosen as fundamental, in the sense that all other statements of the system are to be deduced from them by logical reasoning. *These fundamental statements which are accepted without proof are called axioms.* Their role and significance will be brought out after the reasoning process has been analyzed.

EXERCISES

1. Why must there be undefined terms in a logical system?

2. Define a circle, explaining which of the terms used are undefined.

3. Using the undefined elements *point*, *line*, *distance*, and *angle*, define (*a*) a parallelogram, (*b*) a rhombus, (*c*) a polygon.

1.2 Inductive Reasoning

Reasoning plays an important role in everyday life. In fact, were it not for man's ability to reason, it is doubtful if he could ever have advanced much beyond the primitive stage. Certainly the keener, the more penetrating, the more inclusive the operation of the mind, the greater is the likelihood of man's being able to mold his world into an environment satisfying his needs.

Reasoning also plays a dominant role in the development of a logical system, *inductive* reasoning in discovering theorems, and *deductive* reasoning in proving them.   Inductive reasoning will be discussed first.

Necessity and curiosity have at all times caused people to investigate phenomena and to attempt to find the laws governing the physical universe.   The inundations of the Nile and the need for reestablishing landmarks led the ancient Egyptians to develop simple properties of right triangles.   Curiosity concerning the heavens brought forth various complicated theories about the actions of the planets and the sun. Cures are still being sought for the dread disease cancer.

Very much the same type of reasoning is used in all of these investigations.   A doctor, for instance, arrives at a diagnosis of a specific disease by a careful, systematic investigation of all factors attendant upon the disease.   He notes all symptoms, however trivial, excluding none until it has been proved irrelevant.   He classifies, examines, and combines pertinent facts until he finally reaches the diagnosis which enables him to effect a cure.   Reasoning of this kind is *inductive*.

Often, to verify a conclusion reached by inductive reasoning, the investigator makes repeated experiments.   Sometimes they are carried on for a period of years, as was the case in establishing the laws of astronomy and the laws of heredity.   Galileo also used inductive reasoning when he repeatedly dropped objects from the top of the leaning tower of Pisa to determine his famous law of falling bodies: $s = \frac{1}{2}gt^2$, where s is the distance in feet a body falls in t seconds and g is the gravitational constant whose value is about 32.2 feet per second.

Many other examples may be cited.   There is, for instance, the constantly recurring phenomenon of the sun's rising and setting each day, from which it has been concluded that the sun will rise and set every day in the future.   This does not mean, however, that it is absolutely certain that the sun will rise tomorrow, or a week, or a year, or a million years from now.   Conclusions reached by induction are only statements of what is more or less likely to happen.   If an exception is ever found, either the conclusion is discarded, or laws of probability are used to determine its reliability for future prediction.

EXERCISES

1. Give an original example of the use of induction in arriving at commonly accepted conclusions.

2. If, for the past twenty years, the average temperature in July is higher than that for December, can one conclude that the average temperature for July is always higher than that for December? Give reasons for your answer.

3. If, in each of 500 cases treated, treatment A cured disease B, can one conclude that treatment A will always cure disease B? If treatment A failed to cure disease B on the 501st treatment, should it be abandoned? Give reasons for your answer.

1.3 Some Elementary Logic

To attempt to introduce any but the most elementary principles of logic would be a formidable task, since this science, like geometry, has had a long, interesting period of growth. More than 2,000 years have elapsed since Aristotle first formulated his laws for human reasoning, and in that time radical changes have taken place. Today there is a Whitehead-Russell approach to logic, a formalist approach, headed by Hilbert, and an intuitionist approach headed by Poincaré, Weyl, and others. All have had profound effect on the foundations of mathematics, and at times the effect has been extremely disturbing. The intuitionists' view, for example, if taken literally, would have eliminated a large and important body of mathematics. Current investigations, however, are showing that the different theories are not so far apart as they seemed to be a few years ago. See [6, supplements A, B; 17, pp. 214–217; 62, pp. 247–255].*

There is space here to present only a somewhat modernized version of the classical theory.

Simple Statements and Basic Laws of Reasoning

By a statement is here meant a meaningful sentence such as

$$It\ is\ raining. \tag{1}$$

which has for its negation, or denial, the equally simple statement:

$$It\ is\ not\ raining. \tag{2}$$

Such an expression as "X is an integer" is not a meaningful sentence until X is replaced by a number.

Assuming the customary meaning of truth and falsity in a factual sense, few will deny that, if (1) is true, (2) is false. There seems to be no other possibility, and yet L. E. J. Brouwer, a famous Dutch mathematician of the twentieth century and a leader of the intuitionist school of thought, has raised some questions about this matter when applied to infinite sets.

Absurd as it may seem, Brouwer's position has not been taken with-

* Numbers in brackets refer to entries in the Bibliography.

out sufficient justification.   Not all simple declarative statements can be either affirmed or denied.   This, of course, is true of statements, such as, "World War I was fought to preserve democracy," whose truth or falsity might possibly be a matter of opinion or belief.   It is true also of other types of statements.   Suppose, for example, a man says:

I am lying.

Is his statement true?   If so, he is lying, and his statement is false. Is his statement false?   If so, he is lying, and his statement is true.

Again, suppose that Mr. Smith is a small-town barber who shaves those men and only those men of the town who do not shave themselves.   Which of the following statements is true?

Mr. Smith shaves himself.
Mr. Smith does not shave himself.

Note the dilemma you are in if you attempt to answer this question. If you affirm the first statement and deny the second, you are admitting that Mr. Smith is shaving somebody who shaves himself, contrary to the hypothesis; if you reverse your opinion, affirming the second and denying the first, Mr. Smith is not shaving somebody who does not shave himself, and in this case, too, the hypothesis is contradicted.

Again, can you say which of the following mathematical statements has been proved to be true?

$2^{\sqrt{2}}$ *is a rational number.*
$2^{\sqrt{2}}$ *is not a rational number.*

It will be recalled that a number N is rational if there exist two integers m, n, such that

$$N = \frac{m}{n}$$

As late as the year 1941* no one had found two integers m, n satisfying the condition

$$2^{\sqrt{2}} = \frac{m}{n}$$

but neither had anyone proved that such integers did not exist.   It was therefore impossible to affirm, deny, prove, or disprove either statement.

Fortunately, classical logic avoids controversial questions of such a nature by assuming in advance of an argument that any given statement is either true or false.

The three cornerstone laws of classical Aristotelian logic, called,

* See Harry Pollard, "The Theory of Algebraic Numbers," *Carus Monographs*, no. 9, p. 45.

respectively, the law of *identity*, the law of the *excluded middle*, and the law of *noncontradiction*, are:

1. *A thing is itself.*
2. *A statement is either true or false.*
3. *No statement is both true and false.*

Long-accepted patterns of reasoning are woven around these three laws, but these laws are not usable in vast regions of modern mathematics. In 1912, Brouwer challenged the second law, and a few years later Count Alfred Korzybski, a Polish-American logician, challenged the first. The third law, which deals with the consistency of a system, seems to have held its ground better than the other two laws. Still, in over 2,000 years of trying to reach an agreement on the use of these laws little has been accomplished, except the realization of the need for such an agreement.

Composite Statements

By a composite statement is meant one involving such connecting words as:

$$and, \qquad or, \qquad if\text{-}then$$

Three composite statements are:

$$It \ is \ raining \ \text{and} \ John \ is \ studying. \tag{3}$$
$$It \ is \ raining \ \text{or} \ John \ is \ studying. \tag{4}$$
$$\text{If} \ it \ is \ raining, \ \text{then} \ John \ is \ studying. \tag{5}$$

In modern terminology, (3) is called a $\overset{\wedge}{\text{conjunction}}$, (4) a *disjunction*, and (5) an *implication*. $\longrightarrow$

The *conjunction* of any two statements p, q is the statement "*p and q,*" *which is assumed to be true when both p and q are true; otherwise, it is false.*

Thus, if p is the statement "it is snowing," and q is the statement "the wind is blowing," the conjunction "it is snowing, and the wind is blowing" is true, if it is actually snowing and at the same time the wind is blowing.

The *disjunction* of the statements p, q is the statement "*p or q,*" which *is assumed to be true when at least one of the statements is true; otherwise, it is false.*

The word "or" in this definition is used in a nonexclusive sense, in that the disjunction is still true when *both p and q* are true.

Usually, "or" is used in the exclusive sense illustrated in the statement "either I shall go, or I shall stay," in which the occurrence of one thing excludes the occurrence of the other.

From the new meaning of "or," it follows that the disjunction (4) is *true* if it is raining and John is studying; it is also true if it is not raining and John is studying; and finally, it is true if it is raining and at the same time John is not studying. It is *false*, if it is *not* raining and, at the same time, John is *not* studying.

An implication, such as (5), is a statement of the form "if p, then q" and is written symbolically $p \to q$. *Its precise meaning must be understood.*

What does it mean to say, "If it is raining, then John is studying"? If it is actually raining, the statement states unequivocally that John is studying. But, it may not be raining. If so, no information is given as to whether or not John is studying. It is possible, therefore, that John might be studying even if it were not raining; hence (5) is equivalent to the disjunction:

It is not raining, or John is studying.

and an implication $p \to q$ means that p is false *or* q is true, if "or" is now used in the nonexclusive sense.

The various possibilities of truth and falsity of the statements p, q and the implication $p \to q$ are shown in the table below, where **T** and **F** are the respective abbreviations for true and false.

p	q	$p \to q$
T	T	T
F	T	T
F	F	T
T	F	F

From this table, it is seen that the implication $p \to q$ is true for every combination of truth values of p and q except the one in which p is true and q is false. This means that a *true statement cannot imply a false one.* Thus, the implication:

If the sun shines today, $1 + 1 = 3$.

is false if the sun shines today and is true if the sun does not shine today. This is the case because $1 + 1 = 3$ is false; hence the implication is true only if the statement "the sun shines today" is false.

EXERCISES

1. Give an original example of (*a*) an implication, (*b*) a disjunction, explaining when each is true and false.

2. Check the truth or falsity of each of the following implications:

(a) If New York is a small city, then $2 \times 2 = 4$.

(b) If New York is a large city, then $2 \times 2 = 5$.

(c) If you are a freshman, then the grass is red.

1.4 Deductive Reasoning

Return now to the implication of the preceding section:

$$\textit{If it is raining, then John is studying.} \qquad (1)$$

and, to it, add the further information:

$$\textit{It is raining.} \qquad (2)$$

Then from (1) and (2) one obtains, by the fundamental rule of inference, the definite conclusion:

$$\textit{John is studying.} \qquad (3)$$

and the complete process or argument by which this new statement is obtained is called *deductive reasoning*. Logical and deductive reasoning are here assumed to be synonymous terms.

There are other ways of describing the deductive process. The conclusion (3) is also said to be the inescapable consequence of the hypotheses, or, preferably, (3) is said to be a *valid* conclusion reached by a *valid* argument. It is of the syllogistic type, with its major premise (1), its minor premise (2), and its inescapable conclusion (3) formed from the nutcracker of the other two.

In general, if p and q are any two statements, this type of syllogism, represented symbolically as follows:

$$p \rightarrow q; \qquad p; \qquad \therefore q$$

says in words: If one accepts the truth of the implication $p \rightarrow q$ and also the truth of p, then one must accept the truth of q.

If "not p" denotes the denial of statement p, another equally valid argument is:

$$p \rightarrow q; \qquad \textit{not } q; \qquad \therefore \textit{not } p$$

which, in other words, says that, if one accepts the truth of the implication $p \rightarrow q$ and denies the truth of q, then one must deny the truth of p. This is so, because a true statement cannot imply a false one.

A simple example of this latter type of reasoning is:

If it is snowing, the temperature is below zero.
The temperature is not below zero.
Therefore, it is not snowing.

A mathematical argument of the same type is:

*If in triangle ABC side a equals side b, then the opposite angles A
and B are equal.*
Angle A is not equal to angle B.
Therefore, side a is not equal to side b.

1.5 Abstract Nature of Deductive Reasoning

Form is stressed in the deductive process, rather than content of the
individual statements.   It makes no difference in the validity of the
conclusion whether one is talking about rockets to the moon or about
mere x's and y's devoid of physical meaning.   It makes no difference
whether the conclusion reached is true or false in a factual sense.

Many valid arguments may be given in which the conclusion is true
in some instances and false in others, as the next argument shows:

*If you are a member of this class, you are over twenty-one years
old.*
You are a member of this class.
Therefore, you are over twenty-one years old.

Even though you are actually seventeen years old, you are here
bound to accept the conclusion as true, if you are a member of this
class and have agreed to the original statement.   There is no turning
back.   But this should not be a matter for concern.   You have not
agreed to accept actual, or factual, truth or falsity but simply the
validity (or logical truth) of an abstract argument of the form:

If you are an X, you are a Y.
You are an X.
Therefore, you are a Y.

What is an X? A Y? These questions are immaterial.   It is as
Bertrand Russell once said, somewhat facetiously: "Mathematics is
the subject in which we never know what we are talking about nor
whether what we say is true."   His remark makes sense when one
notes that terms used in the deductive process are undefined, and conclusions rest ultimately on unproved (and sometimes meaningless)
statements.

Conclusions obtained by deductive reasoning are independent of the
nature of the elements involved and are completely detached from
opinions, beliefs, facts, feelings, or emotions in any way connected with
these elements.

1.6. Valid and Invalid Arguments.   A Circle Test for Validity

By an invalid argument is meant one in which the conclusion is not a logical consequence of the hypotheses.   For example, an argument in which one assumes the truth of statement p, from the truth of the implication $p \to q$ and the truth of q, is invalid.   Symbolically, such an invalid argument is written:

$$p \to q; \qquad q; \qquad \therefore p$$

The following is an example of an invalid argument:

If a quadrilateral is a rhombus, its diagonals are perpendicular to each other.
The diagonals of the quadrilateral ABCD are perpendicular to each other.
Therefore, the quadrilateral ABCD is a rhombus.

That the argument is invalid is shown by reference to Fig. 1.1, where the *diamond*-shaped quadrilateral $ABCD$, which is not a rhombus, has

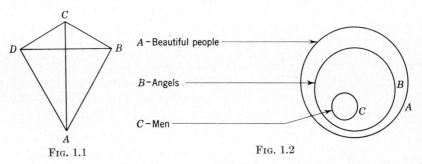

Fig. 1.1   Fig. 1.2

its diagonals perpendicular.   In other words, perpendicularity of its diagonals is no guarantee that a quadrilateral is a rhombus.

There is a simple circle test for determining the validity of a conclusion deduced from statements involving such words as "all," "some," "any," "every," and it will be illustrated for the following argument:

All men are angels.
All angels are beautiful.
All men are beautiful.

In applying the test, it will be assumed that two notions, (1) a set of elements and (2) belonging to a set, are known.

Points of a circle or simply a circle will represent the totality of elements of a certain set, and placing one circle inside another will show graphically that the set of elements represented by the smaller circle belongs to, or is a subset of, the set represented by the larger circle.

Let circle A (Fig. 1.2) represent beautiful people; circle B, angels; and circle C, men. Then, from the first statement in the argument, circle C lies within circle B; and from the second, circle B lies within circle A. Circle C therefore lies within circle A, which means that men form a subset of beautiful people, and the conclusion is therefore valid.

The circle test is applied next to an argument whose validity is to be determined by means of the test.

> *If all good cars are expensive, and*
> *All foreign cars are expensive, then*
> *All foreign cars are good.*

Let circle A (Fig. 1.3) *represent expensive things;* circle B, *good cars;* and *circle C, foreign cars.* Then, from the first statement, circle B lies

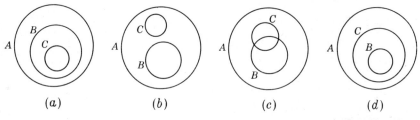

(a)   (b)   (c)   (d)

A – Expensive things
B – Good cars
C – Foreign cars

Fig. 1.3

within circle A; and from the second, circle C lies within circle A; but no information is given as to the position of circle C with respect to circle B. Circle C might lie within circle B (Fig. 1.3a), be external to B (Fig. 1.3b), overlap B (Fig. 1.3c), or include B (Fig. 1.3d). Since one is not forced to accept any particular one of these possibilities and reject the others, the conclusion is invalid.

1.7 Deductive Reasoning in an Elementary Proof

Most mathematical proofs consist of chains of simple deductions from definitions, axioms, and previous theorems. Since the syllogistic form is cumbersome, the argument is usually abbreviated, as shown in the proof of the elementary Euclidean theorem:

If two straight lines intersect, the vertical angles are equal.

The proof will be based on only definitions and axioms. Let $\angle a$ and $\angle c$ be any vertical angles (Fig. 1.4). Then, by definition of a straight angle,

$$\angle a + \angle b = \text{a straight angle} \qquad (1)$$

and

$$\angle b + \angle c = \text{a straight angle} \qquad (2)$$

Therefore, by the axiom that "things equal to the same thing are equal to each other,"

$$\angle a + \angle b = \angle b + \angle c \qquad (3)$$

Hence, by the axiom: "If equals are subtracted from equals, the results are equal,"

$$\angle a = \angle c \qquad (4)$$

Since $\angle a$ and $\angle c$ were any vertical angles (by definition of vertical angles), the theorem is proved.

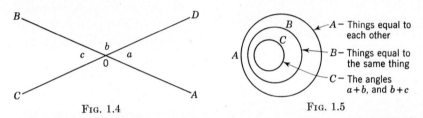

FIG. 1.4   FIG. 1.5

There are two distinct syllogistic arguments in this proof. One of them leads to conclusion (3), the other to conclusion (4). The circle test will be used to check the validity of (3), and the test for (4) left as an exercise. Let circle A (Fig. 1.5) represent the set of things equal to each other; circle B, the set of things equal to the same thing; and, finally, circle C, the pair of angles $a + b$ and $b + c$. Since each of these angles is a straight angle, circle C lies within circle B, and since things equal to the same thing are equal to each other, circle B lies within circle A. Circle C therefore lies within circle A, and the validity of conclusion (3) is established.

1.8. Indirect Method of Proof

Not all proofs proceed in the direct manner just shown. Indirect proofs are extremely powerful and elegant, and yet beginners are reluctant to use them. This type of proof employs the logical principle of the excluded middle, in which an investigator assumes that either a statement or its denial is true. If one is disproved, the other follows.

For example, to show that the sum c of two even integers is an even integer, it is shown that the contrary assumption "c is odd" leads to a contradiction. By the law of the excluded middle, c is either even or odd and since c cannot be odd, then c is even.

Details of the proof, if a and b are the two even integers, are as follows:

If

$$a + b = c$$

then

$$\frac{a+b}{2} = \frac{a}{2} + \frac{b}{2} = \frac{c}{2}$$

But if each of the quantities $a/2$ and $b/2$ is an integer (which must be the case, since a and b are even), their sum is also an integer. The left-hand side of this last equation is therefore an integer; but since, by assumption, c is odd, the right-hand side $c/2$ is not an integer, and a contradiction has been reached.

The indirect method is illustrated again in the following proof of the elementary Euclidean theorem:

If two parallel lines are cut by a transversal, the alternate interior angles are equal.

Let transversal T (Fig. 1.6) cut the two given lines AB and CD in the points M and N. To show that the alternate interior angles AMN and MND are equal, it will be shown that the contrary assumption, i.e., the inequality of these angles, leads to a contradiction. It is assumed in the proof that Theorem 27, Appendix A, has already been proved.

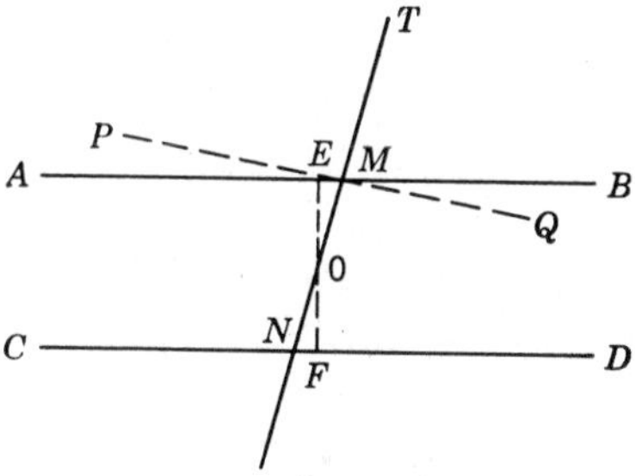

FIG. 1.6

Suppose that the angles AMN and DNM are not equal, and let a line PQ through the point M make angle PMN equal to angle DNM. Then,

PQ is parallel to CD.   (Theorem 27, Appendix A)

and hence through the point M there are two parallels to the line CD. Since this conclusion contradicts the parallel axiom (Sec. 5, Appendix B), the assumption that angles AMN and DNM are unequal is false, and hence, by the law of the excluded middle, these angles are equal.

The student should compare this proof with the much longer direct proof (see Exercise 3 below).

Other examples and discussions of the indirect method may be found in the literature [12, pp. 137–153; 62, pp. 70–72]. In passing, however, it is noted that, although indirect proofs may usually be replaced by direct ones, there are some theorems which by their very nature preclude the possibility of a direct proof [17, pp. 86–87].

EXERCISES

1. Give an indirect proof of the Euclidean theorem:

If the bisectors of two interior angles of a triangle are equal, the triangle is isosceles.
Hint: See [59, p. 141]. How does the indirect proof compare in simplicity with the direct proof?

2. Are the words "invalid" and "false" equivalent in meaning? Explain.

3. Give a direct proof of the Euclidean theorem proved in Sec. 1.8.
Hint: Through the mid-point O of MN (Fig. 1.6), draw a perpendicular to CD, meeting AB and CD in the respective points E and F. Show that the right triangles EOM and ONF are congruent.

Determine which of the following arguments are valid:

4. If Jay is pitching, our team is winning. Our team is winning; therefore Jay is pitching.

5. If Mr. X is President, he is a Democrat. Mr. X is President; therefore Mr. X is a Democrat. (If Mr. X is the present President of the United States, is the conclusion true?)

6. Good canned peaches are expensive, and this can of peaches is good; therefore this can of peaches is expensive.

7. No undergraduates have B.A. degrees. No freshmen have B.A. degrees. Therefore freshmen are undergraduates.

Concluding Remarks

The material here presented is of the selective type, since an exhaustive study of the foundations of geometry is not the primary aim of this work. However, even this brief introduction, supplemented by the discussions in the next chapter, will enable the reader to understand, appreciate, and even anticipate the great changes which have taken place in geometric thinking since Euclid gave to the world his first-class model of a logical system.

SUGGESTIONS FOR FURTHER READING*

Bell, E. T.: "The Search for Truth."
Bentley, A. F.: "Linguistic Analysis of Mathematics."
Black, Max: "The Nature of Mathematics."
Carnap, Rudolf: "Foundations of Logic and Mathematics."
Cohen, M., and E. Nagel: "Introduction to Logic and the Scientific Method."
Columbia Associates of Philosophy: "Introduction to Reflective Thinking."
Keyser, C. J.: "Human Worth of Rigorous Thinking."
Russell, Bertrand: "Introduction to Mathematical Philosophy."
————: "Mysticism and Logic and Other Essays."
Stabler, E. R.: "An Interpretation and Comparison of Three Schools of Thought."
————: "An Introduction to Mathematical Thought."
Tarski, A.: "An Introduction to Logic."
Weyl, Herman: "Mathematics and Logic."
Whitehead, A. N.: "An Introduction to Mathematics."
Wilder, R. L.: "Introduction to the Foundations of Mathematics."

*For complete publication data, see the Bibliography.

Chapter 2

SPECIAL TOPICS OF
AXIOMATIC GEOMETRY

Just as it would be hard to visualize a new, sleek convertible car by examining its various parts, unassembled, so too it is difficult to grasp the idea of a logical system by studying only its component parts, i.e., *undefined elements, axioms,* and *logical reasoning.* It is time now to look at some assembled products.

Euclidean geometry is perhaps one of the most famous examples of a mathematical (logical) system, but there are simpler ones which show the interrelation of the various parts without the added complications of this classical system. A study will be made first of one of these simple systems.

2.1. A Simple Logical System and a Finite Geometry

The elements of a logical system are an ornament S consisting of a set of beads arranged on wires in accordance with the following conditions:

1. Each pair of wires has at least one bead in common.
2. Each pair of wires has not more than one bead in common.
3. Every bead in S is on at least two wires.
4. Every bead in S is on not more than two wires.
5. The total number of wires in S is four.

What does the ornament look like? The answer to this question will be found by deductive reasoning.

A first conclusion, following immediately from statements 1 and 2, is:

6. Every pair of wires in S has one and only one bead in common.

From statements 3 and 4 follows the next conclusion:

7. Every bead in S is on two and only two wires.

In less formal and more familiar language, statements 6 and 7 declare that through two different beads there passes one and only one wire and that there are not more than two wires through each bead.

The number of beads in the ornament will be determined next.

As a result of statement 5, there are exactly four wires in the ornament. Let (i,j) denote the bead common to the wires W_i and W_j. Then, since two things can be selected from four in six different ways, there are six beads in the ornament. Denote them by $A(1,2)$, $B(1,3)$, $C(1,4)$, $D(2,3)$, $E(2,4)$, $F(3,4)$.

By statement 2 these six beads are all distinct, and another conclusion is:

8. There are exactly six beads in S.

It is noted next that on each wire there is a bead common to (i.e., that lies on) each of the remaining wires. Thus, on W_1 are the beads $(1,2)$, $(1,3)$, $(1,4)$, and hence another conclusion is:

9. There are three beads on each wire.

If now beads are represented by points and wires by curved lines, an ornament S satisfying the nine statements just given is shown in

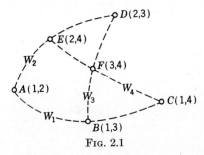

Fig. 2.1

Fig. 2.1, and the power of logical reasoning has been demonstrated.

A definition is introduced next. *Parallel beads are those not connected by a wire.* For example, points C and D of Fig. 2.1 are parallel beads. From this definition follows the next conclusion:

10. Each bead in S has exactly one bead parallel to it.

To prove this last statement, let a bead, say A, lie on the two wires W_1 and W_2. The remaining two wires then determine exactly one bead F, and no wire passes through both the beads A and F.

The logical system just described and represented in Fig. 2.1 may be linked with axiomatic geometry by replacing the words ornament, bead, wire by the geometric terms shown in column I of the table below.

	I	II
Ornament	Plane	Plane
Bead	Point	Line
Wire	Line	Point

Statements 1 to 5 then become:

*a.*1. Each pair of lines in the plane has at least one point in common.

*a.*2. Each pair of lines in the plane has not more than one point in common.

a.3. Every point in *S* is on at least two lines.

a.4. Every point in *S* is on not more than two lines.

a.5. The total number of lines in *S* is four.

A geometry based on these five statements, which we may now term axioms, is a highly restricted one called a finite geometry, because there are only a finite number of points on each line. The latter statement is a consequence of the fact that there were only a finite number of beads on each wire of ornament *S* and of the fact that logical reasoning is independent of the nature of the elements satisfying axioms of a logical system. Whether one reasons about beads on a wire or points on a line is immaterial.

Another finite geometry could be obtained by making the replacements of terms shown in column II of the table just given. Conclusion 10 would then read:

Each line in S has exactly one line parallel to it.

EXERCISES

1. How many sets of parallel beads are there in the ornament *S* of Fig. 2.1? Name them.

2. Does the figure consisting of the four points and four lines shown in Fig. 2.2 satisfy the five axioms just given? Give reasons for your answer.

3. Consider a system *S* whose undefined elements, *point* and *line*, satisfy the following axioms:

b.1. There exist exactly three distinct points.

b.2. Two distinct points determine a line.

b.3. Not all points are on the same line.

b.4. Two distinct lines determine at least one point.

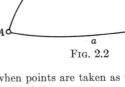

Fig. 2.2

Show that Axioms *b*.1 to *b*.4 are satisfied when points are taken as the symbols *A*, *B*, *C* and lines are vertical columns in the table below:

A B C

B C A

Prove that two distinct points determine at most one line.

4. Suppose that a group of politicians have assembled in a room *S* of New York City and have formed committees for campaign work in accordance with the following instructions, called axioms:

Axioms

c.1. If A_1 and A_2 are distinct (different) men of *S*, there exists at least one committee containing both A_1 and $A_{\_}$.

c.2. If A_1 and A_2 are distinct men of S, there is not more than one committee containing both A_1 and A_2.

c.3. Any two committees have at least one man of S in common.

c.4. There exists at least one committee.

c.5. Every committee contains at least three men of S.

***c*.6.** Not all men serve on the same committee.

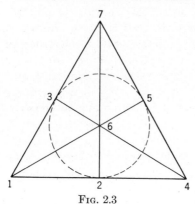

FIG. 2.3

c.7. No committee contains more than three men of S.

Prove that *there are only seven men in the room.* *Hint:* See [75, pp. 38–42].

5. Replace the words "men" and "committee" by the respective words "point" and "line" in each of the axioms of Exercise 4. Then there results a finite geometry which is represented graphically in Fig. 2.3. Prove that in this geometry:

(*a*) Each line contains three points and on each point are three lines.

(*b*) S contains only seven points and seven lines. (Points 2, 3, 5 lie on the dotted line of the figure.)

6. Replace Axiom *c*.7 of Exercise 4 by the new axiom: "No committee contains more than four men of S." How does this replacement affect the number of men in S? *Hint:* See [67, Vol. 1, p. 6].

2.2. Concerning the Selection of Axioms

What dictates the axioms of a logical system? In the system just described, it was a physical ornament. Euclidean geometry too had its practical origin. There now seems little doubt that Euclid's purpose in compiling his "Elements" was to derive properties of physical space from a few explicitly stated definitions and assumptions. To this end, he started with 10 assumptions (see Appendix A) concerning the undefined elements, point, line, and plane; but it was their physical counterparts, i.e., a dot, a ray of light, and a smooth mirrorlike surface, which helped him to formulate these axioms.

For example, the axiom which says that a straight line may be drawn between two points is a highly idealized description of what happens when the point is replaced by a dot and the line by a taut string, ray of light, or rigid rod.

It is true that many physical lines may be drawn through two pencil dots; nevertheless, if the dots gradually become smaller and smaller, these different lines will eventually appear to coincide. By progressive abstraction, then, one finally reaches a statement concerning elements which are stripped of all physical meaning.

An immediate advantage of such a process should be obvious. Statements, or axioms, concerning undefined elements are no longer subject to those experimental errors made when dealing with physical objects, nor is the reasoning process distorted by what seems to be true of these physical elements.

2.3. Applied Geometry

It is not at all necessary that axioms of an abstract system describe properties of space or physical objects. Sheer fantasy, a powerful imagination, or a stroke of genius may be at work in the process of selecting axioms for a given system. If later, physical elements are found to have properties satisfying axioms of the abstract system, so much the better, for mathematics lives by virtue of its wide applicability. Theorems of the abstract system may then be used to describe additional and perhaps hidden properties of these physical elements. The abstract system is then said to be applied, and in such a case it is perfectly legitimate to speak of an axiom as a "self-evident fact" and of theorems as true, meaning that they are experimentally verifiable.

The application process has been illustrated in Boolean algebra, a highly abstract system which was constructed without reference to physical reality and later put to practical use in the construction of electric circuits and computing machines. The importance of these machines in modern research cannot be overestimated. The high-speed mathematical "brain," built at the Institute for Advanced Study by von Neumann, played a vital role in the hydrogen-bomb race. Calculations that would have required several lifetimes were made in a matter of months. In fact, it took this machine, believed to be the world's fastest and most accurate, six months to complete the computations on mathematical equations of the bomb.

2.4. Another Logical System: Projective Geometry

Another example of a logical system is projective geometry. It is not, as many think, an extension of Euclidean geometry but is, rather, a perfectly logical system based on sets of axioms about the undefined elements, point, line, and plane, and on two undefined relations, incidence and separation. One set of axioms, called incidence axioms, deals with the property of a point being on a line. Another set, called existence axioms, deals with the actual existence of points and lines. These and other axioms of the system will be listed later when projective geometry is studied. At this point, attention is being directed to the fact that *different sets of axioms lead to different geometries*.

2.5. Properties of a Set of Axioms

It is now generally agreed that, if a set of axioms is to lead to results of any importance in either an abstract or an applied sense, the set should be *consistent*, *complete*, and *independent*.

A set of axioms is said to be consistent if no two statements of the system contradict each other or if, of any two contradictory statements in the system, at least one cannot be proved.

A set of axioms is called complete if, of any two contradictory statements involving terms of the system, at least one statement can be proved in the system.

A set of axioms is said to be independent if it does not contain a single superfluous statement, i.e., a statement which can be deduced from the remaining axioms and which might therefore be counted among the theorems.

If the logical system is a geometry which is to be applied, it is important that axioms correspond well with properties of physical objects representing the undefined terms.   In this way one arrives at theorems further describing these elements.

The questions of consistency of a geometry and of the independence of its axioms are, of course, related ones.   To show that an axiom y of a system S is *independent* of the other axioms of the system, it is sufficient to show that these residual axioms and a new axiom y' that directly contradicts axiom y form a *consistent* system S'.   For, if axiom y were not independent of the other axioms of system S, it could be deduced as a theorem.   The new system S' would then contain both axiom y and a contradiction of this axiom and hence be inconsistent.

As for consistency, that is still a highly controversial question. Great and serious efforts have been made in recent time to find consistency proofs, at least for axioms of algebra, but complete success in this direction has not yet been attained.

2.6. Logical Defects in Euclid

Despite Euclid's unquestioned ability, his geometry does not satisfy the present-day requirements for logical rigor.   It contains flaws.   To begin with, tacit assumptions are not permitted in a logical system; yet Euclid made quite a few of them.   For example, he used the assumption that a line is infinite in extent in some of his proofs, but no such assumption was made in his axioms, nor is this property of a line a consequence of his other axioms.   A line can be extended indefinitely in either direction, but this does not mean that the line is infinite.   A geometry will be studied later in which a line may be extended indefinitely in either direction and still be finite in length (see Chap. 15). Again, in his proof by superposition, Euclid gives evidence of assuming facts not so stated in his axioms. The assumptions concerning congruence form an important part of any system of axioms for geometry. Lack of appreciation of this fact lies at the root of the difficulty involved in the method of superposition. In proving the congruency of two triangles having two sides and the included angle of the one equal to two sides and the included angle of the other, Euclid actually regarded one triangle as being moved in order to make it coincide with the other. He thereby tacitly assumed motion of figures without their deformation, and completely ignored the fact that points are undefined elements. If, on the other hand, one considers geometry as an applied science in which figures are capable of displacement, or motion, there cannot be ignored the modern physical notion that the dimensions of bodies in motion are not the same as when they are at rest. Relativity theory has shown that space and time cannot be separated.

When Euclid constructed lines and circles to prove the existence of certain figures, he tacitly assumed their intersection points. In a rigorous development, the existence of these points must be either proved or guaranteed by means of an axiom. Euclid's failure to do this was later corrected by an axiom (see Sec. 6, Appendix B), which ascribes to all lines and circles that characteristic called *continuity*.

Another main defect in Euclid's system was his almost complete disregard of such notions as the *two sides of a line* and the *interior of an angle*. Without the clarification of these ideas, absurd consequences result such as the paradox discussed in the next section.

2.7. A Paradox

Proof will now be given of the following theorem:

Theorem 2.1 (*A Paradox*)
  Every triangle is isosceles.

Theorems upon which the proof is based will be found in Appendix A.

In the triangle ABC (Fig. 2.4) let O be the point of meeting of the perpendicular bisector OD of side BC and the bisector AO of angle A. Draw line OE perpendicular to side

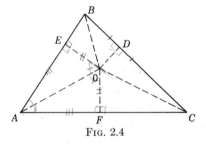

Fig. 2.4

AB and line OF perpendicular to side AC. Join O to the points B and C. Then, the right triangles AOF and AOE are congruent, and hence

$$OE = OF \qquad \text{and} \qquad AE = AF$$

The right triangle OCF is therefore congruent to the right triangle OBE, and hence $EB = CF$. Consequently

$$AE + EB = AB = AF + FC = AC$$

and the triangle ABC is isosceles.

To explain the paradox, try constructing your own figure and see the position of point O with respect to the triangle ABC. Does it fall within or without the triangle? (See the following exercise.)

EXERCISE

Show that point O of Fig. 2.4 falls without the triangle ABC. Does $AB = AC$ in this case? Prove your answer.

2.8. Hilbert's Axioms for Euclidean Geometry

Primarily through the works of such men as Pasch, Peano, and Hilbert, logical defects in Euclid have been removed and the whole of Euclidean geometry placed on a sound, logical basis.

About the best of the modified sets of axioms for Euclidean geometry is Hilbert's (see Appendix B), first published in his book "The Foundations of Geometry," in which he considers a class of undefined elements called points and certain undefined subclasses of these points called straight lines and planes. His axioms concerning these elements are divided into the five subsets:

1. Incidence axioms
2. Order axioms
3. Congruency axioms
4. An axiom of parallels
5. Axiom of continuity

From them, all theorems of elementary Euclidean geometry may be deduced.

The assumptions, in which congruence is taken as one of the fundamental undefined notions, were probably suggested by the extensive controversies which took place as to whether Euclid regarded the idea of congruence or the idea of motion as fundamental.

Order axioms eliminate the possibility of paradoxes such as the one just given.

2.9. Concerning a Revision of an Order Axiom

In an early edition of his work "The Foundations of Geometry," Hilbert gave an order axiom containing *more assumptions* than are found in the corresponding axiom of the seventh edition of the same work. The reasoning which dictated this change is to be studied here. It is an excellent example of a more complicated type of logical reasoning than any presented thus far. By fine detailed workmanship, a conclusion is reached which permits a simplification of the original axiom.

Two sets of axioms will be employed in the simplification process, and three axioms of the first set are:

Incidence Axioms

I.1. *Given any two points A, B, there exists a line (a) lying on A and B.*

I.2. *Given A, B, there exists at most one line (a) lying on A, B.*

I.3. *There are at least two points which lie on a given line. There are at least three points which do not lie on a line.*

The second set of axioms is concerned with order relations. Each of these order axioms is stated and carefully analyzed.

Order Axioms

O.1. *If the point B is between A and C, then A, B, C are three different points of a line, and B is also between C and A.*

This axiom implies that the term "between" is used only for points on a line and states that the relative position of points A and C does not affect B's property of lying between A and C.

O.2. *Given points A and B on a line, there exists at least one point C such that B lies between A and C.*

This axiom guarantees the existence of at least three points on a line and allows one to refrain from setting stronger existence postulates in the incidence axioms. Note, in this connection, Axiom I.3, which guarantees the existence of three points, but not all on a line.

O.3. *Given points A, B, C on a line, then at most one of these points lies between the two others.*

This axiom together with Axioms O.1 and O.2 permit the following definition:

An interval consists of those points B of line AC for which B is between A and C, and B is called an interior point of the interval.

O.4. *(Pasch's Axiom.)   If a line α intersects one side AB of a triangle (Fig. 2.5) in a point X between A and B and if α does not pass
through C, then there exists on α a
point Z between C and B, or a
point Y between A and C.*

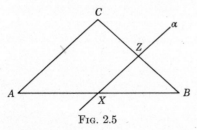

Fig. 2.5

From Axiom O.1, it is seen that
α cannot pass through A or B; but,
thus far, it is not known whether
there exists any point X between A
and B.   Axiom O.2 assumes only
the existence of a point on AB extended.   The next theorem disposes
of this question.

Theorem 2.2 *(Existence Theorem)*

*If A and B are any two distinct points on a line, there exists a point
X between A and B.*

PROOF.   From Axiom I.3, there exists a point E outside of the line
AB (Fig. 2.6) and, by Axiom I.1, a line AE connecting the points A
and E.   Draw the line AE.   Ac-
cording to Axiom O.2, there exists a
point F on AE and a point G on FB
such that E is between F and A and
B is between G and F.   Draw lines
GE and FB.

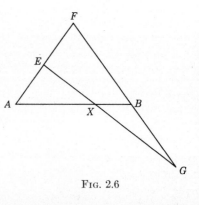

Fig. 2.6

Line GE does not pass through
any of the points A, B, F.   If it
passed through A, point E would
coincide with A, since EG intersects
AF in E and therefore cannot intersect this line in a second point (Axiom
I.2); if GE passed through B, it
would be the line BGE and would intersect AF in F and not E.   The
same would be true if GE passed through F.

Now, since E is a point between A and F, Pasch's axiom may be
applied to the triangle ABF.   According to this axiom, GE must meet
either line AB in a point X between A and B or line FB in a point Y
between F and B.   But the point Y cannot exist, since the intersection of lines FB and GE is, by construction, the point G; and by
Axiom O.3, point G cannot lie between F and B, since B lies between
F and G.   Therefore line GE intersects AB in a point X between A
and B, and the theorem is proved.

Corollary 1

If two points P and P' are on the same side of a line α and if point Q is on the same side of α as P, then Q and P' are also on the same side of α.

PROOF.   If line α (Fig. 2.7) were to intersect $P'Q$, it would follow from Pasch's axiom that it would also intersect PP' or PQ in an interior point.

Corollary 2

If P and P' are points on different sides of α and if point Q is on the same side of α as P, then P' and Q are on different sides of α.

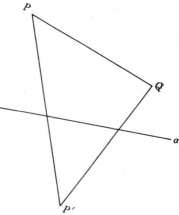

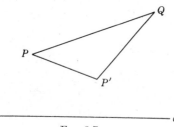

Fig. 2.7   Fig. 2.8

PROOF.   By Pasch's axiom, α must intersect QP' (Fig. 2.8) in an interior point, since, by hypothesis, it intersects PP' but not PQ.

Attention is called now to the distinction between Axiom 0.2 and the existence theorem just proved.   In the former, a point C is assumed to exist on the line segment AB extended, and it can then be proved that there exists a point on AB between A and B.   Originally the second order axiom read as follows:

If A and C are two points of a straight line, then there exists at least one point B between A and C and at least one point D so situated that C lies between A and D (Fig. 2.9).

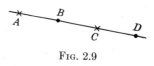

Fig. 2.9

In the light of the existence theorem just proved, this original axiom contained an assumption which was a logical consequence of the other axioms.   It was therefore removed, and the assumption became a theorem.   This means that Hilbert's original set of order axioms was not *independent*.

EXERCISES

1. When is one axiom of a set said to be independent of the others?
2. When is a set of axioms said to be consistent?
3. In what sense are independence and consistency properties related?
4. How can one axiom be proved to be independent of others of a set? *Hint:*
See [75, pp. 69–70].
5. What is meant by a paradox?
6. Name two defects in Euclid's early system.
7. What is meant by applied geometry?
8. Is it true that, through a point P not on a line L, there is only one parallel
to a line? Explain.

2.10. Euclidean Geometry and the Physical Universe

Early Egyptian geometry, it will be recalled, arose from man's experience with physical objects and was, consequently, a collection of useful facts. For example, to form a right angle, the Egyptians took a closed circle of rope and divided it by means of three knots into three parts whose lengths were in the ratio $3:4:5$. Then three men, each holding a knot, stretched the rope tight, thus forming a triangular figure, as shown in Fig. 2.10.

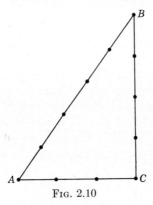

FIG. 2.10

In this way, east and west lines were drawn on the earth's surface after north and south had been determined by astronomical observations. The perpendicular lines thus obtained were probably used by the Egyptians as guides in constructing their pyramids and temples.

There were also numerical formulas for finding certain areas. For instance, the area of a flat field in the form of an isosceles triangle was found by multiplying the length of one of the equal sides by one-half the length of the base; and the area of a circular plot with a radius of r feet was taken to be

$$\tfrac{256}{81}r^2 = 3.16049r^2$$

These and the other formulas developed by practical methods sufficed for the ancient Egyptians, but not for the more advanced Greeks. With considerable wealth at their command and with slaves to do their menial work, the Greeks had ample opportunity for developing their superb talents for abstract reasoning. No more perfect target could be found than these crude formulas of the ancient Egyptians. By forming abstract ideas of such things as points, lines, and planes, stating axioms about these elements, and reasoning logically from these axioms, the Greeks developed their abstract science.

Unfortunately, this linking of geometry, the experimental science, with geometry, the logical abstract science, led scientists and the world in general to the erroneous belief that Euclid's geometry was simply the abstract, mathematical formulation of the laws of the universe and hence that there could exist one and only one geometry.

Many examples seem to support this belief, even today. An actual flat triangular lot is supposed to have the properties of its mathematical idealization, i.e., a figure bounded by three lines. So, in the triangular lot, as in the mathematical triangle, the greatest angle lies opposite the greatest side, the sum of its angles is 180°, and if the triangular lot is a right triangle, the square of its hypotenuse is equal to the sum of the squares of the other two sides, as in a theorem of Euclidean geometry. In this, and in many other ways, the world applies Euclidean geometry to the physical universe.

Are all such applications mute evidence of the Euclidean character of space? The answer is no. If careful experiments should seem to indicate, for instance, that the hypotenuse of a right-triangular lot is 5 yards long, when the other two sides are 3 and 4 yards, respectively, that would not be convincing evidence of the Euclidean character of space; for measurements are only approximations, and small errors in measurements cannot be detected. In fact, it is now known that Euclidean geometry is only a first approximation to the geometry of the physical universe. It is highly inadequate for many of the theoretical investigations of the twentieth-century scientists.

SUGGESTIONS FOR FURTHER READING

Cooley, H., D. Gans, M. Kline, and H. Wahlert: "Introduction to Mathematics," 2d ed., Chap. 24.
Eddington, Sir Arthur S.: "The Nature of the Physical World."
———: "Space, Time and Gravitation."
Forder, H. G.: "The Foundations of Euclidean Geometry."
Heath, T. L.: "The Thirteen Books of Euclid's Elements."
MacNeish, H. F.: Four Finite Geometries.
Poincaré, H.: "The Foundations of Science."
———: "Science and Hypothesis."
Robinson, G. de B.: "The Foundations of Geometry."
Russell, Bertrand: "The Foundations of Geometry."
———: "Our Knowledge of the External World."
Young, J. W.: "Lectures on Fundamental Concepts of Algebra and Geometry."
Young, J. W. A.: "Monographs on Modern Mathematics,"

Chapter 3

MENELAUS' AND CEVA'S THEOREMS

In marked contrast with Euclid's geometry, which is concerned almost exclusively with such metric concepts as lengths, angles, areas, and volumes, there was developed about 150 years ago a new science called projective geometry. In its purest form this science is free of the distance concept.

Roots of the new geometry are found in ancient theorems dealing with nonmetric properties of figures, e.g., theorems concerning points all lying on the same line, or lines all passing through the same point, but the real significance of such theorems was not recognized until hundreds of years later. They are now seen to be in reality projective theorems in a Euclidean setting.

An initial study of these Euclidean forerunners of projective geometry will serve a double purpose. It will bring to the attention of the reader some Euclidean theory of more than passing interest, and at the same time it will show how a new science is born.

After projective geometry has been developed as a logical system in its own right, quite independent of the early science, Euclidean and projective geometries will be linked by certain advanced viewpoints. Such a plan follows closely the historical and painstakingly slow development of the new science.

Two classical theorems which will introduce nonmetric theory in a metric setting are those of Menelaus and Ceva. The first of these theorems was discovered by Menelaus of Alexandria about 100 B.C. and was rediscovered about 1800 years later by Ceva, an Italian engineer and mathematician. In 1678, Ceva published both Menelaus' theorem and a very closely connected one of his own, named, after him, Ceva's theorem.

Reference theorems of Euclidean geometry upon which proofs depend will be found in Appendix A.

3.1. Menelaus' Theorem

Menelaus' theorem is concerned with the collinearity of points, one on each side of a triangle. Before stating the theorem, two definitions are recalled:

Two points A, B on a directed line determine a line segment whose length AB is positive if the direction from A to B agrees with the positive direction on the line and negative if the direction from A to B is in the contrary direction.

Thus $$AB = -BA$$

A point P divides a directed line segment AB into the ratio r, where

$$r = \frac{AP}{PB}$$

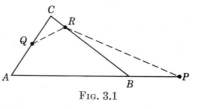

Fig. 3.1

The ratio r is therefore positive or negative according as P is an internal or an external point of division. For example, point P of Fig. 3.1 divides side AB of triangle ABC into a negative ratio, whereas point Q divides side AC into a positive ratio.

A statement and proof of Menelaus' theorem follows:

Theorem 3.1 (Menelaus' Theorem)

A necessary and sufficient condition that three points P, Q, R on the respective sides or extensions of the sides BC, CA, AB of the triangle ABC be collinear is that

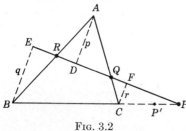

Fig. 3.2

$$\frac{AR}{RB} \cdot \frac{BP}{PC} \cdot \frac{CQ}{QA} = -1 \quad (1)$$

The necessity of this condition will be established by showing that, when the points P, Q, R are collinear, condition (1) is satisfied.

Let p, q, r (Fig. 3.2) denote the lengths of the respective perpendiculars AD, BE, CF to the line PQR, called a transversal of the triangle ABC. Suppose first that none of the points P, Q, R coincides with a vertex. Then, since triangle ADR is similar to triangle BER, triangle CFP to triangle BEP, and triangle CFQ to triangle ADQ, and since only one of the points P, Q, R, say P, is an external point of division (Axiom 3.4, Appendix B),

$$\frac{AR}{RB} = \frac{p}{q} \qquad \frac{CQ}{QA} = \frac{r}{p} \qquad \frac{BP}{PC} = -\frac{q}{r}$$

Hence $$\frac{AR}{RB} \cdot \frac{BP}{PC} \cdot \frac{CQ}{QA} = -\frac{p\,q\,r}{q\,r\,p} = -1$$

and the necessity of condition (1) has been proved.

The sufficiency of the given condition will be established by show-ing that from (1) follows the collinearity of the points P, Q, R.

Let a line through two of the points Q, R meet side BC in a point P'. Then from the proof just given

$$\frac{AR}{RB} \cdot \frac{BP'}{P'C} \cdot \frac{CQ}{QA} = -1$$

which, when divided by (1), gives

$$\frac{BP'}{P'C} = \frac{BP}{PC}$$

Hence $$\frac{(BP' + P'C)(= BC)}{P'C} = \frac{(BP + PC)(= BC)}{PC}$$

from which it follows that

$$P'C = PC$$

But points P' and P are both on BC extended. Therefore P' coincides with P, and the three points P, Q, R are collinear. Thus the theorem is proved when no point coincides with a vertex.

When a transversal passes through a vertex, say C, the points P and Q coincide, $PC = CQ = 0$, and condition (1) is meaningless. But then it follows that

$$AR \cdot BP \cdot CQ = RB \cdot PC \cdot QA$$

since each side has the value zero. This last statement illustrates, therefore, *the alternative form of Menelaus' theorem*:

If three points, taken on the three sides of a triangle, determine on these sides six segments such that the product of three nonconsecutive segments is equal to the product of the other three, the three points are collinear, and conversely.

3.2. Applications

It is now possible to bring a number of apparently isolated theorems of elementary geometry into one general class, i.e., those dealing with the collinearity of a triple of points, one on each side of a triangle.

One general method for handling all such theorems is provided by Menelaus' theorem. The method and the great unifying power of this classical theorem are illustrated next.

Theorem 3.2

The internal bisectors of two angles of a triangle and the external bisector of the third angle meet their respective opposite sides in three collinear points.

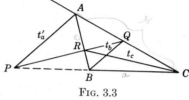

FIG. 3.3

PROOF. In the triangle ABC (Fig. 3.3) let a, b, c denote lengths of sides opposite the respective vertices A, B, C and let the external bisector t'_a of angle A and the two internal bisectors t_b, t_c of angles B and C meet their opposite sides in the respective points P, Q, R. Then, from Theorem 59, Appendix A, it follows that

$$\frac{AR}{RB} = \frac{b}{a} \qquad \frac{CQ}{QA} = \frac{a}{c} \qquad \frac{BP}{PC} = -\frac{c}{b}$$

and hence

$$\frac{AR}{RB} \cdot \frac{CQ}{QA} \cdot \frac{BP}{PC} = -\frac{a}{c}\frac{b}{a}\frac{c}{b} = -1$$

By Menelaus' theorem, the points P, Q, R are therefore collinear, and the theorem is proved.

Theorem 3.3

Tangents to the circumcircle of a triangle at its vertices intersect the opposite sides in three collinear points.

PROOF. Let the tangents to the circumcircle of triangle ABC at vertices A, B, C (Fig. 3.4) cut the sides BC, CA, AB at the points P, Q, R, respectively, and let a, b, c denote the lengths of the respective sides BC, CA, AB. Then, in the triangles ABP and ACP, $\angle P$ is common and $\angle PAB = \angle C$ (Theorems 57 and 55,

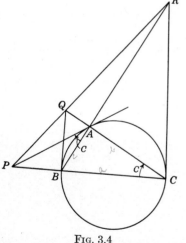

FIG. 3.4

Appendix A). These triangles are therefore similar, and $AP/PB = b/c$.

Hence

$$\left(\frac{AP}{PB}\right)^2 = \left(\frac{b}{c}\right)^2 \qquad (1)$$

but, from Theorem 61, Appendix A,

$$(AP)^2 = |PB| \cdot |CP| \qquad (2)$$

and hence, substituting (2) in (1) and simplifying,

$$\left|\frac{CP}{PB}\right| = \frac{b^2}{c^2}$$

Similarly,

$$\left|\frac{AQ}{QC}\right| = \frac{c^2}{a^2} \qquad \left|\frac{BR}{RA}\right| = \frac{a^2}{b^2}$$

Therefore

$$\left|\frac{AQ}{QC}\right| \cdot \left|\frac{CP}{PB}\right| \cdot \left|\frac{BR}{RA}\right| = \frac{c^2}{a^2} \cdot \frac{b^2}{c^2} \cdot \frac{a^2}{b^2} = 1$$

and since points P, Q, R are all external points of division,

$$\frac{AQ}{QC} \cdot \frac{CP}{PB} \cdot \frac{BR}{RA} = -1$$

From Menelaus' theorem it then follows that the points P, Q, R are collinear, and the theorem is proved.

EXERCISES

Using Menelaus' theorem, prove each of the following theorems:

1. The external bisectors of a triangle meet the opposite sides in three collinear points.

2. If on the sides AB, AC of the triangle ABC are taken two equal segments AE and AF, the median issued from A divides the segment EF into the ratio of these sides.

3. A', B', C' are the mid-points of the sides BC, CA, AB of the triangle ABC. If line AA' meets the line $B'C'$ in point P and if the line CP meets AB in Q, then $AQ/AB = \frac{1}{3}$.

4. In the triangle ABC whose medians meet in the point G, AG is produced to a point P so that $GP = AG$. Then the parallels through P to CA, AB, and BC meet BC, CA, AB in three collinear points.

5. The incircle of the triangle ABC touches sides BC, CA, AB at the points X, Y, Z, respectively. YZ is produced to meet BC in K; then

$$\frac{BX}{CX} = \frac{BK}{CK}$$

6. If A, C, E are points of one line and B, D, F points of another, the intersections of the pairs AB, DE; BC, EF; CD, FA are collinear points. (This theorem was discovered by Pappus of Alexandria about 300 A.D.)

3.3. Ceva's Theorem

Ceva's theorem, which deals with the concurrency of triads, or triples, of lines, one through each vertex of a triangle, is stated next and proved easily with the aid of Menelaus' theorem.

Theorem 3.4 (Ceva's Theorem)

A necessary and sufficient condition that the three lines which join the points L, M, N on the respective sides BC, CA, AB of the triangle ABC to the opposite vertices be concurrent is that

$$\frac{AM}{MC} \cdot \frac{CL}{LB} \cdot \frac{BN}{NA} = 1 \qquad (1)$$

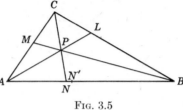

FIG. 3.5

The necessity of this condition is shown first. Let each of the points L, M, N be distinct from a vertex of the triangle, and let P be the point of meeting of the lines AL, BM, and CN (Fig. 3.5). Then, in the triangle BNC cut by the transversal AL,

$$\frac{BA}{AN} \cdot \frac{NP}{PC} \cdot \frac{CL}{LB} = -1 \qquad \text{(Theorem 3.1)}$$

and similarly, in the triangle ACN cut by the transversal BM,

$$\frac{AM}{MC} \cdot \frac{CP}{PN} \cdot \frac{NB}{BA} = -1$$

Hence, multiplying these last two equations and simplifying,

$$\frac{AM}{MC} \cdot \frac{CL}{LB} \cdot \frac{BN}{NA} = 1 \qquad (2)$$

Thus the necessity of (1) has been proved.

To show the sufficiency of this condition, let two of the three lines AL, BM, and CN, say BM and AL, intersect in a point P, and let the line CP meet AB at a point N'. Then

$$\frac{AM}{MC} \cdot \frac{CL}{LB} \cdot \frac{BN}{N'A} = 1 \qquad \text{(Why?)}$$

which, when divided by (1) and simplified, gives

$$\frac{BN'}{N'A} = \frac{BN'}{NA} \qquad (3)$$

from which it follows that points N' and N coincide. The lines AL,

BM, and CN are therefore concurrent and the sufficiency of condition (1) has been established.

If any of the points L, M, N is a vertex, (1) is meaningless, but then

$$AM \cdot CL \cdot BN = MC \cdot LB \cdot NA$$

since each side of this equation has the value zero, and there is thus illustrated the *alternative form of Ceva's theorem:*

> *If three points taken on the three sides of a triangle divide these sides into six segments so that the product of three segments having no common end is equal to the product of the remaining three, the lines joining the three points to the opposite vertices of the triangle are concurrent, and conversely.*

3.4. Applications

Ceva's theorem, like Menelaus', unifies a number of elementary theorems dealing with the concurrency of triads of lines, each line being through a different vertex of a triangle, such as the altitudes or medians of a triangle, or the bisectors of its angles. In elementary geometry, these theorems are usually given separate treatments. Ceva's theorem, on the other hand, provides a standard method for handling all of them. The method is illustrated in what follows.

Theorem 3.5

> *The medians of a triangle are concurrent.*

The proof is simple. If A', B', C' are the mid-points of the sides BC, CA, AB of triangle ABC (Fig. 3.6),

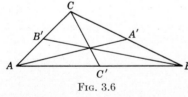

FIG. 3.6

$$\frac{BA'}{A'C} = \frac{CB'}{B'A} = \frac{AC'}{C'B} = 1$$

and hence

$$\frac{BA'}{A'C} \cdot \frac{CB'}{B'A} \cdot \frac{AC'}{C'B} = 1$$

It then follows from Ceva's theorem that the medians AA', BB', and CC' are concurrent.

The next theorem was proved in the early part of the nineteenth century by Joseph D. Gergonne, a French mathematician.

Theorem 3.6

> *The lines joining the vertices of a triangle to the points of contact of the opposite sides with the incircle of the triangle are concurrent.*

PROOF.   Let X, Y, Z (Fig. 3.7) be the points of contact of the incircle of triangle ABC with its sides BC, CA, AB.   Then, from Theorem 53, Appendix A,

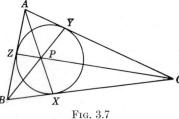

$$AZ = AY$$
$$BZ = BX$$
$$CX = CY$$

and hence

$$\frac{AZ}{ZB} \cdot \frac{BX}{XC} \cdot \frac{CY}{YA} = 1$$

FIG. 3.7

By Ceva's theorem, the lines AX, BY, CZ are therefore concurrent at a point P.   *Point P is called the Gergonne point of the triangle.*

3.5. The Pedal-triangle Theorem

The next theorem depends on the following definition:

A line drawn from the vertex of a triangle to a point on the opposite side of the triangle is called a Cevian.

The points L, M, N in Fig. 3.5 are the feet of the corresponding Cevians, and triangle LMN is called the *pedal triangle* of the point P.

Theorem 3.7

If one of three concurrent Cevians in a given triangle is an altitude, this altitude bisects the corresponding angle of the pedal triangle.

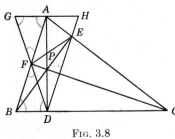

FIG. 3.8

PROOF.   Let AD be an altitude of the triangle ABC (Fig. 3.8) and let the three Cevians AD, BE, CF meet at a point P.   To prove that AD bisects the angle FDE, draw a line through A parallel to BC and let this parallel intersect DE and DF in the respective points H and G.   Then, triangle AFG is similar to BFD, and triangle AEH to triangle DEC.   (Why?)   Hence

$$\frac{AF}{FB} = \frac{AG}{BD} \quad \text{and} \quad \frac{CE}{EA} = \frac{DC}{AH} \tag{1}$$

But, by Ceva's theorem,

$$\frac{AF}{FB} \cdot \frac{BD}{DC} \cdot \frac{CE}{EA} = 1 \tag{2}$$

Substitution of (1) in (2) then gives

$$\frac{AG}{BD} \cdot \frac{BD}{DC} \cdot \frac{DC}{AH} = 1$$

from which

$$AG = AH$$

Since the perpendicular from vertex D of triangle GDH bisects the base GH, it bisects also the angle FDE.   Thus the theorem is proved.

3.6. Desargues' Theorem

The next theorem will appear later in an entirely different setting (see Sec. 7.6).

Theorem 3.8 (Desargues' Theorem)

If two triangles $A_1B_1C_1$ and $A_2B_2C_2$ are so situated that the three lines A_1A_2, B_1B_2, C_1C_2 joining corresponding vertices are concurrent, the pairs of corresponding sides will intersect in three collinear points.

PROOF.   If in Fig. 3.9 the lines A_1A_2, B_1B_2, C_1C_2 joining corresponding vertices of the two triangles $A_1B_1C_1$ and $A_2B_2C_2$ meet at a point O, and if A', B', C' are the respective points of intersection of corresponding sides B_1C_1, B_2C_2; A_1C_1, A_2C_2; A_1B_1, A_2B_2, the theorem will be proved by showing that the points A', B', C' are collinear.   This is done by the use of Menelaus' theorem.

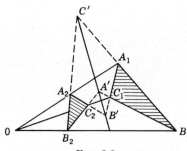

FIG. 3.9

In the triangle A_2B_2O cut by the transversal A_1B_1C' it follows from Menelaus' theorem that

$$\frac{A_2C'}{C'B_2} \cdot \frac{B_2B_1}{B_1O} \cdot \frac{OA_1}{A_1A_2} = -1 \tag{1}$$

Similarly, in the triangle B_2C_2O cut by the transversal B_1C_1A',

$$\frac{B_2A'}{A'C_2} \cdot \frac{C_2C_1}{C_1O} \cdot \frac{OB_1}{B_1B_2} = -1 \tag{2}$$

and, in the triangle A_2C_2O cut by the transversal A_1C_1B',

$$\frac{C_2B'}{B'A_2} \cdot \frac{A_2A_1}{A_1O} \cdot \frac{OC_1}{C_1C_2} = -1 \tag{3}$$

When (1), (2), and (3) are multiplied together and the result simplified,

$$\frac{A_2C'}{C'B_2} \cdot \frac{B_2A'}{A'C_2} \cdot \frac{C_2B'}{B'A_2} = -1$$

It then follows, when Menelaus' theorem is applied to the triangle $A_2B_2C_2$, that the points A', B', C' are collinear, and thus the theorem is proved.

Other applications of Ceva's theorem are found in the following set of exercises.

EXERCISES

1. Using Ceva's theorem, prove that the following triads of lines in a triangle are concurrent: (a) the altitudes; (b) the interior bisectors of the angles of the triangle; (c) the exterior bisectors of two angles and the interior bisector of the third angle.

2. Show that the centroid, i.e., the point of meeting of the medians of a triangle, is the only point which divides its Cevians into segments having equal ratios.

3. Show that, if one of three concurrent Cevians bisects the corresponding angle of the pedal triangle, it is an altitude of the given triangle.

Chapter 4

HARMONIC ELEMENTS AND CROSS RATIO

HARMONIC ELEMENTS

Another elementary theory to be treated later in an entirely different setting is concerned with a set of points and a set of lines called harmonic points and harmonic lines. The appearance of these elements in Euclidean geometry and their reappearance later in a basic role in modern, nonmetric developments of projective geometry (see Chap. 8) will serve to emphasize some of the striking differences between the new and the old systems. It is especially interesting that the germ of the modern development was known to an ancient people. Modern man exploits the findings of the past.

4.1. Harmonic Points

It is known from elementary geometry that, in the triangle APB (Fig. 4.1), the interior and exterior bisectors of angle P meet the opposite side AB in the respective points C and D which divide the side internally and externally into the same ratio. This means that, when all segments are directed,

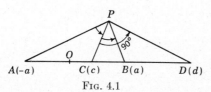

Fig. 4.1

$$\frac{AC}{CB} = -\frac{AD}{DB} \qquad (1)$$

where a symbol such as AC denotes the length of the directed line segment whose extremities are A and C.

The four points A, B, C, D are then said to be *harmonic*, in accordance with the following formal definition:

Four collinear points A, B, C, D are harmonic when (1) is satisfied. The pair of division points C, D of the line segment AB are called harmonic conjugates of the points A, B.

Since from (1) there follows also the relation

$$\frac{CA}{AD} = -\frac{CB}{BD} \tag{2}$$

the points A, B may also be considered division points of the line segment CD.

The definition of harmonic points automatically divides the four given points A, B, C, D into the pairs A, B and C, D. Either pair is called the *harmonic-conjugate pair of the other pair*. Also, a division point, say C, of one pair is said to be the *harmonic conjugate of the other division point D with respect to the points A, B*.

The symbol $H(AB,CD)$ denotes that pairing of the harmonic points in which the pair A, B are harmonic conjugates of the pair C, D.

The name harmonic is well chosen. In music, when a set of strings of the same diameter and material are stretched to uniform tension and made to vibrate at one time, three or more strings produce harmony if their lengths form a harmonic progression. It is shown in Theorem 4.1 of the next section that the directed line segments AC, AB, AD of the harmonic points $H(AB,CD)$ form a harmonic progression.

4.2. Basic Theorems

Three theorems showing useful properties of harmonic points will be presented next.

Theorem 4.1

In the harmonic set of points $H(AB,CD)$, the directed line segments AC, AB, AD form a harmonic progression, and conversely.

PROOF. It is known from algebra that three quantities x, y, z form a harmonic progression when

$$\frac{2}{y} = \frac{1}{x} + \frac{1}{z}$$

Hence, to prove the theorem, it must be shown that

$$\frac{2}{AB} = \frac{1}{AC} + \frac{1}{AD}$$

and conversely.

Because the segments AB, AC, AD are directed, it follows from Eq. (1) of the preceding section that $CB/AC = BD/AD$, and hence

$$\frac{CB}{AB \cdot AC} = \frac{BD}{AB \cdot AD} \tag{1}$$

But, $CB = AB - AC$ $BD = AD - AB$

Substitution of these expressions in (1) then gives

$$\frac{AB - AC}{AB \cdot AC} = \frac{AD - AB}{AB \cdot AD}$$

which may be written:

$$\frac{1}{AC} - \frac{1}{AB} = \frac{1}{AB} - \frac{1}{AD}$$

or

$$\frac{2}{AB} = \frac{1}{AC} + \frac{1}{AD}$$

A reversal of these arguments gives the proof of the converse theorem, and thus Theorem 4.1 is proved.

Theorem 4.2

In the harmonic set of points $H(AB,CD)$ the distance from the mid-point O of the line segment AB to each of its extremities is the mean proportional between the distances from O to the points C and D, and conversely.

PROOF. In the harmonic set of points $H(AB,CD)$, Fig. 4.1, let a and $-a$ denote the respective distances of points B and A from the mid-point O of line segment AB and let c, d be the respective distances of points C, D from this same point O. Then, the lengths of the segments AC, CB, AD, and DB are

$$\begin{aligned} AC &= c + a & CB &= a - c \\ AD &= d + a & DB &= a - d \end{aligned} \tag{2}$$

From the definition of harmonic points

$$\frac{AC}{CB} = \frac{DA}{DB} \tag{3}$$

Substitution of (2) in (3) then gives the relation

$$\frac{c + a}{a - c} = -\frac{d + a}{a - d}$$

which when simplified reduces to

$$a^2 = cd \quad \text{or} \quad a = \sqrt{cd}$$

A reversal of these arguments gives the proof of the converse theorem, and thus Theorem 4.2 is proved.

Theorem 4.3

If O is a point outside the line of the harmonic points H(AB,CD) and if a parallel to OA through B meets the lines OC and OD in points P, Q, respectively, then PB = BQ, and conversely.

PROOF. Let points of Fig. 4.2 satisfy conditions of the theorem and the lengths of all line segments be positive. Since triangles AOC and BPC are similar,

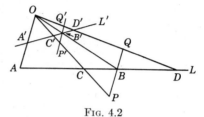

FIG. 4.2

$$\frac{AC}{CB} = \frac{AO}{PB}$$

and, since triangles AOD and BQD are similar,

$$\frac{AD}{DB} = \frac{AO}{BQ}$$

But, the harmonic points $H(AB,CD)$ satisfy the relation

$$\frac{AC}{CB} = \frac{AD}{DB}$$

Therefore

$$\frac{AO}{PB} = \frac{AO}{BQ}$$

from which it follows that

$$PB = BQ$$

A reversal of these arguments gives the proof of the converse theorem, and thus Theorem 4.3 is proved.

4.3. Harmonic Lines

Suppose that the lines OA, OB, OC, OD of Fig. 4.2 are cut by a second line L' in the respective points A', B', C', D'; then the new set of points are also harmonic, as will now be shown.

If a line through point B' of Fig. 4.2 is parallel to PQ and intersects lines OP and OQ in the respective points P' and Q', then, from the theory of similar triangles,

$$\frac{OB'}{OB} = \frac{P'B'}{PB} = \frac{Q'B'}{BQ}$$

But

$$PB = BQ$$

and hence

$$P'B' = B'Q'$$

Therefore, the points A', B', C', D' form the harmonic set $H(A'B', C'D')$ (Theorem 4.3), and if A', B', C', D' are called the projections on L' of the points A, B, C, D, proof has been given of the following significant theorem:

Theorem 4.4

The projection of a harmonic set of points is a harmonic set of points.

Because of this theorem, any transversal of the lines OA, OB, OC, OD of Fig. 4.2, except a line through O, will cut these lines in a harmonic set of points. A set of harmonic lines may therefore be defined as follows:

A set of four coplanar, concurrent lines is harmonic if a transversal cuts them in a harmonic set of points.

From this definition and Theorem 59, Appendix A, then follows the next theorem:

Theorem 4.5

The interior and exterior bisectors of an angle form with the sides of the angle a harmonic set of lines.

4.4. Applications

Some unusual and unexpected places in which harmonic elements appear are shown in the three theorems presented below, the first of which makes use of the following definition:

Two intersecting circles are orthogonal if tangents at a point of intersection are perpendicular.

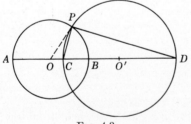

Fig. 4.3

Theorem 4.6

If two circles are orthogonal and if a diameter AB of one circle meets the other circle in the points C and D, the points A, B, C, D are harmonic.

PROOF. Let the given circles with centers at O and O' intersect at a point P (Fig. 4.3). Then,

$$(OP)^2 = OC \cdot OD \qquad \text{(Why?)}$$

But $$OA = OP$$

and hence

$$(OA)^2 = OC \cdot OD$$

It then follows from Theorem 4.2 that the points A, B, C, D are harmonic.

Theorem 4.7

If a chord BD of a circle is perpendicular to a diameter AC, the lines joining any point P of the circle to the points A, B, C, D form a harmonic set of lines.

PROOF. Since the lines AC and BD (Fig. 4.4) are perpendicular, arcs BC and CD are equal (Theorem 50, Appendix A), and hence

$$\angle BPC = \angle CPD$$

Line PC is therefore the interior bisector of $\angle BPD$. Also, since AC is a diameter,

$$\angle APC = 90° \qquad \text{(Theorem 55, Appendix A)}$$

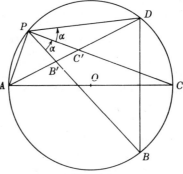

FIG. 4.4

The line PA is therefore an exterior bisector of $\angle BPD$. From Theorem 4.5 it then follows that the lines PA, PB, PC, PD are harmonic, and thus the theorem is proved.

Theorem 4.8

Concurrent lines through the vertices A, B, C of a triangle meet the opposite sides BC, CA, AB in the points L, M, N, respectively. If the line MN meets the side BC at point L', the points B, C, L, L' are harmonic.

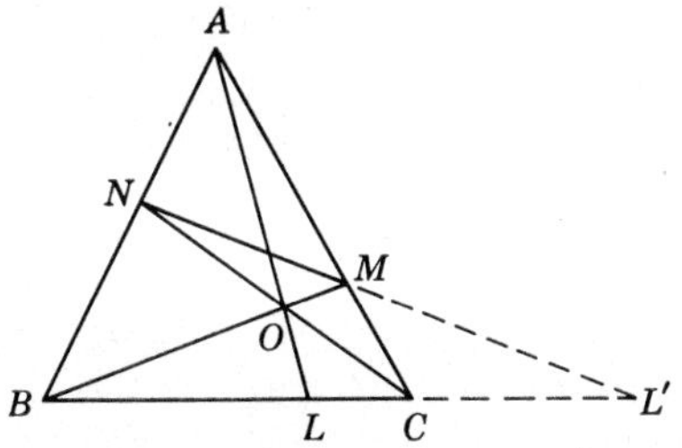

FIG. 4.5

PROOF. Let points and lines of Fig. 4.5 satisfy conditions of the theorem.

Since the lines AL, BM, CN of Fig. 4.5 are concurrent,

$$\frac{AN}{NB} \cdot \frac{BL}{LC} \cdot \frac{CM}{MA} = 1 \qquad \text{(Theorem 3.4)} \qquad (1)$$

Also, since the points L', M, and N are collinear,

$$\frac{AN}{NB} \cdot \frac{BL'}{L'C} \cdot \frac{CM}{MA} = -1 \qquad \text{(Theorem 3.1)} \qquad (2)$$

Hence, dividing (1) by (2) and simplifying,

$$\frac{BL}{LC} = -\frac{BL'}{L'C}$$

It then follows from the definition of harmonic points that B, L, C, L' are harmonic points, and the theorem is proved.

EXERCISES

1. Show that, if three points A, B, C of a harmonic set are given, it being known which two form a pair, the fourth point D is uniquely determined.

2. Given four harmonic lines with the members of one pair at right angles to each other. Show that the other pair make equal angles with them. *Hint:* Note in Fig. 4.4 the acute angles PC forms with rays PB and PD, etc.

3. If A, B, C, D and A', B', C', D' are two sets of harmonic points such that the lines AA', BB', CC' are concurrent at a point O, prove that the line DD' also passes through O.

4. The bisector of angle A of the triangle ABC meets the opposite side in the point P. Points Q and R are the feet of the perpendiculars from B and C to AP. Show that the set of points A, P, Q, R is harmonic.

5. Points L, M, N are the mid-points of the sides BC, CA, AB of the triangle ABC. Lines LA and LN meet BM in points X and Y. Show that the set of points M, X, Y, B is harmonic.

6. A line through the mid-point A' of the side BC of the triangle ABC meets the side AB in point F, side AC in G, and the parallel through A to side CB in E. Show that the set of points A', E, F, G is harmonic.

7. Prove that the line through the points of contact of the incircle with two sides of a triangle cuts the third side in a point which forms a harmonic set of points with the point of contact and the other two vertices on this third side.

8. Three lines, one issuing from each vertex of a triangle, are concurrent. The harmonic conjugate of the intersection of each line with the opposite side with respect to the other two vertices is determined. Prove that these three conjugate points are collinear.

CROSS RATIO

The relation (1) of Sec. 4.1 between the harmonic points $H(AB,CD)$ may be rewritten in the form

$$\frac{AC/CB}{AD/DB} = -1$$

in which the left-hand side is seen to be the quotient of two ratios and the right-hand side to have the special value -1. It is proposed to investigate this double ratio for values other than -1. The double ratio is called the cross ratio of the four points.

4.5. Cross Ratio of Four Points; of Four Lines

If A, B, C, D are four distinct collinear points, the cross ratio λ of these points is given by the expression:

$$\lambda = \frac{\text{ratio into which } C \text{ divides line segment } AB}{\text{ratio into which } D \text{ divides line segment } AB}$$

$$= \frac{AC/CB}{AD/DB}$$

Since all segments are directed, λ is a signed quantity. If the division points C, D are both external (Fig. 4.6a) or both internal (Fig.

C A B D	A C D B	A C B D
$\lambda > 0$	$\lambda > 0$	$\lambda < 0$
(a)	(b)	(c)

Fig. 4.6

4.6b), λ is positive. If one of the points of division is internal and the other external (Fig. 4.6c), λ is negative.

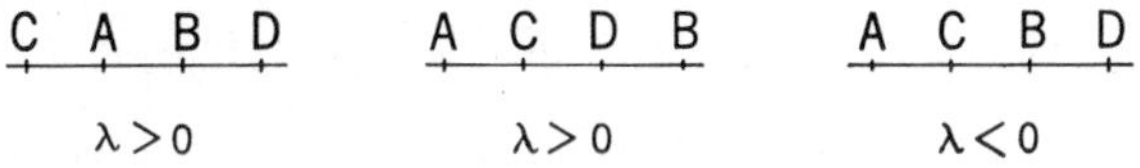

This definition automatically separates the four points into pairs, so that points A, B of one pair are extremities of a line segment, while the remaining points C, D are its division points. Such a grouping is indicated by the symbol $R(AB,CD)$, or simply (AB,CD). Thus

$$R(AB,CD) = (AB,CD) = \frac{AC/CB}{AD/DB} = \frac{AC \cdot DB}{CB \cdot AD} = \lambda$$

4.6. Cross Ratio Unchanged on Projection

A basic theorem concerning cross ratio is the following:

Theorem 4.9

The cross ratio of four points on a line is unchanged under projection.

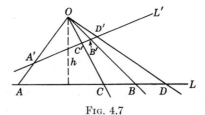

Fig. 4.7

PROOF. If λ is the cross ratio (AB,CD) of the points A, B, C, D of a line L (Fig. 4.7) and if λ' is the cross ratio of their projections on a second line L', it will be shown first that the numerical values $|\lambda|$ and $|\lambda'|$ are equal.

Let h denote the distance from the center O of projection to the line

L containing the points A, B, C, D, and let all quantities be considered positive. Then, in the triangles OAC, OCB, OAD, and ODB,

$$\text{Area } \Delta OAC = \tfrac{1}{2}h \cdot AC = \tfrac{1}{2}OA \cdot OC \sin \angle AOC$$
$$\text{Area } \Delta OCB = \tfrac{1}{2}h \cdot CB = \tfrac{1}{2}OB \cdot OC \sin \angle COB$$
$$\text{Area } \Delta OAD = \tfrac{1}{2}h \cdot AD = \tfrac{1}{2}OA \cdot OD \sin \angle AOD$$
$$\text{Area } \Delta ODB = \tfrac{1}{2}h \cdot DB = \tfrac{1}{2}OD \cdot OB \sin \angle DOB$$

from which it follows that

$$\frac{AC/CB}{AD/DB} = \frac{AC}{CB} \cdot \frac{DB}{AD} = \frac{OA \cdot OC \sin \angle AOC \cdot OD \cdot OB \sin \angle DOB}{OB \cdot OC \sin \angle COB \cdot OA \cdot OD \sin \angle AOD}$$
$$= \frac{\sin \angle AOC \cdot \sin \angle DOB}{\sin \angle COB \cdot \sin \angle AOD} = \lambda$$

The value λ of the cross ratio, therefore, depends only on the angles subtended at point O by the segments AC, CB, DB, AD. But these angles are the same for any four points into which these points are projected. Therefore $|\lambda| = |\lambda'|$.

The invariance of the sign of λ is shown next. From Hilbert's order axioms (see Appendix B), it follows that, if three points A, C, B are in the order A, C, B, their projected points A', C', B' are in the same order: A', C', B'. This means that the sign of the ratio AC/CB is the same as the sign of the ratio $A'C'/C'B'$, and since the sign of each ratio in the double ratio, or cross ratio, is invariant on projection, so also is their quotient. Thus the proof of Theorem 4.9 is completed.

Because of this theorem, any transversal of four coplanar, concurrent lines, called *a pencil of lines,* will cut these lines in a set of points whose cross ratio is the same for all positions of the transversal except the one through the point of meeting of the lines. The point of concurrency of the four lines is called *the vertex of the pencil,* and *the cross ratio of this pencil of lines is by definition the cross ratio of the points in which these lines are met by a transversal.*

More specifically, if four concurrent lines L_1, L_2, L_3, L_4 are cut by a transversal in the respective points A_1, A_2, A_3, A_4, the cross ratio (L_1L_2,L_3L_4) of this pencil of lines equals the cross ratio (A_1A_2,A_3A_4) of the four points A_1, A_2, A_3, A_4.

4.7. The Twenty-four Cross Ratios

Since any one of four distinct points may be paired with any of the remaining ones, and each such pairing determines a resulting cross ratio, order is an essential part of the definition of cross ratio.

Does the possibility of arranging 4 elements in 24 different ways mean that there are 24 possible cross ratios for any given 4 points or 4 lines? This question will be investigated next.

Let a, b, c, d represent the distances of the collinear points A, B, C, D from a reference point O of the line. Then, the lengths of the directed line segments AC, CB, AD, DC are as follows:

$$AC = c - a \qquad CB = b - c \qquad AD = d - a \qquad DB = b - d$$

and the value of the cross ratio (AB,CD) then becomes

$$(AB,CD) = \frac{(c - a)(b - d)}{(b - c)(d - a)}$$

Only algebraic manipulation of this formula is needed to prove the next three theorems.* They may also be proved (see Exercise 1 below) by making use of the following relation among four collinear points A, B, C, D:

$$AB \cdot CD + AC \cdot DB + AD \cdot BC = 0$$

Theorem 4.10

The cross ratio (AB,CD) does not change its value if the pairs of elements are interchanged, or if the order of pairs is reversed.

Thus $(AB,CD) = (CD,AB) = (BA,DC) = (DC,BA) = \lambda$

Theorem 4.11

The reversal of the order in one pair changes the value of the cross ratio (AB,CD) to its reciprocal.

Thus $(BA,CD) = (CD,BA) = (AB,DC) = (DC,AB) = \dfrac{1}{\lambda}$

Theorem 4.12

The cross ratios of the ordering in which the pairs are split are $(AC,BD) = 1 - \lambda$ and $(AD,BC) = (\lambda - 1)/\lambda$.

Thus $(AC,BD) = (BD,AC) = (CA,DB) = (DB,CA) = 1 - \lambda$

and $(AD,BC) = (BC,AD) = (CB,DA) = (DA,CB) = \dfrac{\lambda - 1}{\lambda}$

From these theorems it follows that a cross ratio of a given four points has one of the following six values:

$$\lambda \qquad \frac{1}{\lambda} \qquad 1 - \lambda \qquad \frac{1}{1 - \lambda} \qquad \frac{\lambda - 1}{\lambda} \qquad \frac{\lambda}{\lambda - 1}$$

* For a proof of these theorems in parabolic geometry, see Sec. 13.5.

These six quantities are distinct unless the points are harmonic, in which case, they reduce to the three values

$$-1 \qquad 2 \qquad \tfrac{1}{2}$$

EXERCISES

1. Prove Theorems 4.10 to 4.12, using the relation among the four collinear points A, B, C, D: $AB \cdot CD + AC \cdot DB + AD \cdot BC = 0$. *Hint:* See [59, pp. 105–106].

2. Give the values of (AD,BC) and (BC,AD) for the four collinear points $A(1)$, $B(2)$, $C(5)$, $D(-2)$, where each number associated with a point is its distance from a fixed point of the line.

3. (*a*) Are the points $A(-1)$, $B(0)$, $C(1)$, $D(10)$ harmonic? Why? (*b*) Give the coordinate of the harmonic conjugate of B with respect to A and C.

4. Prove that, when three collinear points A, B, C and also their cross ratio (AB,CD) are given, the fourth point D is uniquely determined.

4.8. Cross-ratio Properties of the Circle

Of the many possible applications of cross ratio, two special cross-ratio properties of the circle have been selected for presentation here. These properties will be linked later with the projective theory of conics.

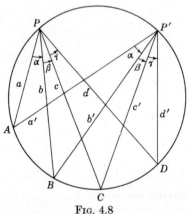

FIG. 4.8

Property 1

If any four points of a circle are joined to a fifth point, the cross ratio of the resulting pencil of lines is independent of the position of the fifth point.

PROOF. In Fig. 4.8 four fixed points A, B, C, D of a circle are joined to any fifth point P of this same circle by the lines a, b, c, d. The cross ratio $P(ac,bd)$ of the resulting pencil of lines has a value dependent only on the angles α, β, γ subtended at P by the arcs AB, BC, and CD. Since these arcs are fixed, the angles do not change as P moves on the circle. Thus when P is at the point P' and the rays a, b, c, d are the new rays a', b', c', d', the angles subtended at P' by arcs AB, BC, CD are again α, β, γ, and the new cross ratio $P'(a'c',b'd')$ equals the old $P(ac,bd)$. The cross ratio $P(ac,bd)$ is therefore independent of the position of the point P, and property 1 is proved.

The next cross-ratio property of the circle is much like the first except that the roles of point and line are interchanged. Whereas in the first property four points are given, in the second, four tangents (lines) to a circle are given. These four tangents are cut by any fifth tangent in four points whose cross ratio is to be examined as the fifth tangent moves on the circle. This cross ratio will be shown to be independent of the position of the fifth tangent.

Property 2

The cross ratio of the points of intersection of any four fixed tangents to a circle with a fixed tangent is the same for every position of the fifth tangent.

PROOF. Let a, b, c, d in Fig. 4.9 be the fixed tangents at the respective points A, B, C, D of the circle. Suppose the fixed tangents a and

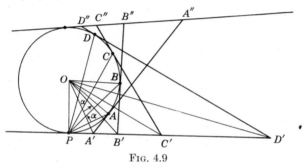

FIG. 4.9

b at the points A and B meet the fifth tangent p at a point P in the respective points A' and B'. Since OA' and OB' are the respective perpendicular bisectors of PA and PB (Why?), the angle APB equals the angle $A'OB' = \alpha$. Similarly, angle $B'OC'$ equals angle $BPC = \beta$, and angle $C'OD'$ equals the angle $CPD = \gamma$. Since the angles α, β, γ do not change as the fifth tangent moves on the circle, and since the cross ratio $(A'C', B'D')$ of the four points in which the four fixed tangents meet the fifth tangent depends only on the angles α, β, γ, property 2 is proved.

Further applications of cross ratio will be found in the following exercises.

EXERCISES

1. If A, B, C, D are the points in which the concurrent rays a, b, c, d meet a line L, and if a line through B parallel to the line c intersects lines a and d in the points A' and D', respectively, prove that the cross ratio (BC, AD) equals the ratio $A'B/D'B$.

2. If A, B, C are three collinear points, construct the point D on their line such that the cross ratio (AB,CD) equals the cross ratio (BA,CD).

3. If, through the mid-point M of the chord AB of a circle, two other chords CD and EF are drawn, and if DE and CF intersect AB in G and H, prove that M is also the mid-point of the segment GH.

4. If six points on a line correspond in pairs, A to A', B to B', and C to C', and if

$$OA \cdot OA' = OB \cdot OB' = OC \cdot OC'$$

where O is a point collinear with these six points, show that the cross ratio (AB',BC) equals the cross ratio $(A'B,B'C')$.

5. Show that points of intersection of opposite sides of a hexagon inscribed in a circle are collinear. *Hint:* See [59, p. 108].

Chapter 5

INVERSION THEORY

Another elementary theory of more than passing interest, and one to be used later (see Sec. 14.4), is that of inversion in a circle. It is the joint discovery early in the nineteenth century of J. W. Stubbs and J. R. Ingram, two Fellows of Trinity College, Dublin.

Originally, the theory seems to have been a sort of generalization of reflection in a straight line. In Fig. 5.1, point P has for its reflection *in a line L* the point P' such that L is the perpendicular bisector of PP'. When L is replaced by a circle with center O and radius r, and when P' is a point on OP such that

$$OP \cdot OP' = r^2$$

P is said to be reflected *in the circle* (Fig. 5.2). Points P and P' are then called inverse points with respect to the circle.

Reflection in a circle and its resulting theory have had many fruitful results. In 1873, the theory was put to practical use by a French army officer, Peaucellier, when he invented an instrument called, in his honor, the Peaucellier cell. This is the linkage which finally solved the problem of constructing a straight line without the use of a straightedge.

A practical need for a straight-line construction had arisen when the inventor James Watt attempted to link the piston of his steam engine to a point on the flywheel in such a way that the rotation of the fly-wheel would move the piston along a straight line. Watt succeeded in obtaining only an approximate solution, and despite the efforts of many workers in the field, the problem remained unsolved until Peaucellier invented his very simple linkage which transformed circular into rectilinear motion. (The usual processes of drawing a straight line presuppose the existence of a straightedge already constructed [35].

Peaucellier's invention, which makes use of inversion theory, is only another one of the many instances in which highly abstract mathematical theory has been put to practical use.

The theory was later discovered independently by the famous mathematician and physicist Sir William Thomson (Lord Kelvin). By its aid, Sir William gave geometrical proofs of some of the most difficult propositions in the mathematical theory of elasticity.

An introduction to the new idea follows.

5.1. The Circle of Inversion. Inverse Points

In what follows, unless it is otherwise stated, O is the center and r the radius of a given circle, denoted $(O)_r$ and called the circle of inversion.

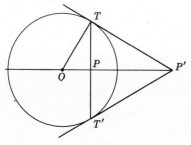

FIG. 5.2

If P is not the center O of circle $(O)_r$, the inverse of point P with respect to circle $(O)_r$ is, by definition, the point P' (Fig. 5.2) lying on the line OP, on the same side of O as P and such that:

$$OP \cdot OP' = r^2$$

From this definition it follows that to each point P of the plane, except O, there corresponds an inverse point P'. Moreover, when OP is greater than r, OP' is less than r, and the effect of an inversion is merely an interchange of the inside and outside of the circle. When OP equals r, OP' also equals r. Hence points of the circumference, and only those points, remain fixed, or invariant, under inversion.

In what follows, frequent use is made of the following two elementary theorems:

Theorem a

Two triangles which have an angle of one equal to an angle of the other and the including sides proportional are similar.

Theorem b

A necessary and sufficient condition that a quadrilateral $ABB'A'$ be inscriptible (i.e., have its vertices on a circle) is that a pair of opposite angles be supplementary.

5.2. Theorem Concerning Inverse Points

A first useful theorem concerning two pairs of inverse points is.

Theorem 5.1

If A, A' and B, B' are two pairs of inverse points, a circle through three of these four points passes through the fourth point.

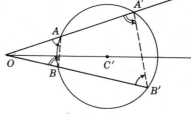

PROOF. Since points A, A' and B, B' (Fig. 5.3) are two pairs of inverse points,

$$OA \cdot OA' = OB \cdot OB' = r^2$$

Fig. 5.3

The triangles OAB and $OA'B'$ therefore have angle A in common and including sides proportional.   Hence by Theorem a of Sec. 5.1 the triangles are similar, and

$$\angle OAB = \angle OB'A' \qquad \angle OBA = \angle OA'B'$$

The angles ABB' and $AA'B'$ are therefore supplementary.

It then follows from Theorem b of Sec. 5.1 that the quadrilateral $ABB'A'$ is inscriptible, and thus the theorem is proved.

EXERCISES

1. Prove Theorem b of Sec. 5.1.
2. Show that, if point P is outside the circle of inversion, its inverse point P' lies on the chord of contact of tangents to the circle from P.
3. Construct the inverse of a point P within the circle of inversion.

5.3. The Inverse of a Line

When a point P moves on a curve, its inverse point P' will move on a curve called the inverse of the given curve.   It is proposed to investigate next the inverse of a point which moves on a straight line, according as the line does or does not pass through the center of inversion.

From the definition of inverse points, it follows that, if P is any point on a line through the center of inversion, its inverse point P' lies on the same line, and thus points of this line are simply interchanged by the inversion.   Thus a first theorem concerning the inverse of a line is:

Theorem 5.2

The inverse of a line through the center O of inversion is the line itself.

The next theorem shows the effect of inversion on a line *not through the center of inversion.*

Theorem 5.3

The inverse of a line not through the center O of inversion is a circle through O.

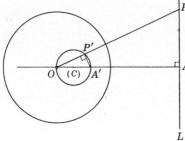

Fig. 5.4

PROOF.   Let A be the foot of the perpendicular from O to the given line L (Fig. 5.4), and let A' be its inverse point with respect to circle $(O)_r$.   If P' is the inverse of any other point P of L, the triangles OAP and $OA'P'$ are similar, and angle $OAP = 90° =$ angle $OP'A'$. Point P' therefore lies on a circle whose diameter is OA' (Why?), and the theorem is proved.

5.4. The Inverse of a Circle

In discussing the inverse of a circle it will be necessary, as in the case of straight lines, to distinguish between circles through the center of inversion and circles not through the center of inversion.   A first theorem concerning the inverse of a circle is:

Theorem 5.4

The inverse of a circle through the center O of inversion is a line not through O.

The theorem is illustrated in Fig. 5.4 where the inverse of the circle on OA' as a diameter is the line L.   A reversal of the arguments in the proof of Theorem 5.3 gives the proof of the theorem (see Exercise 1 below).

A second theorem concerning the inverse of a circle is:

Theorem 5.5

The inverse of a circle not through the center O of inversion is another circle not through O.

PROOF.   To obtain the inverse of a circle (A) not through the center O of inversion (Fig. 5.5), draw a line through O intersecting the given circle in points P and Q. Then if P' and Q' are their respective inverse points,

$$OP \cdot OP' = r^2 = OQ \cdot OQ' \tag{1}$$

and if OT is the tangent from O to the circle (A), then from Theorem 61, Appendix A,

$$OP \cdot OQ = (OT)^2 \tag{2}$$

From (1) and (2) it then follows that

$$\frac{OP'}{OQ} = \frac{OQ'}{OP} = \left(\frac{r}{OT}\right)^2 \tag{3}$$

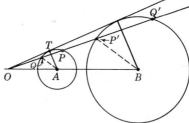

Fig. 5.5

Now, through P' draw a line parallel to QA meeting OA at point B. Then, the triangles OQA and $OP'B$ are similar, and

$$\frac{OP'}{OQ} = \frac{OB}{OA} = \left(\frac{r}{OT}\right)^2 = \frac{P'B}{QA} = \text{a constant} \tag{4}$$

B is therefore a point on line OA at a fixed distance from the point A, and since $P'B$ is also a constant (Why?), point P' moves on a circle whose center is B. Thus the theorem is proved.

A useful theorem which links inverse points with orthogonal circles is:

Theorem 5.6

A circle orthogonal to the circle of inversion inverts into itself, and, conversely, a circle through a pair of inverse points is orthogonal to the circle of inversion.

PROOF. Let T be the point of meeting of circle $(O)_r$ and an orthog-

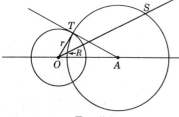

Fig. 5.6

onal circle with center at A (Fig. 5.6). If a line through O meets this orthogonal circle at points R and S, then

$$OR \cdot OS = (OT)^2 = r^2$$

and hence a point R of this circle has its inverse on the same circle. Conversely, when this condition is satisfied, OT is tangent to circle (A), and a circle through points R and S is orthogonal to circle $(O)_r$. Thus the theorem is proved.

EXERCISES

1. Prove that the inverse of a circle through the center O of inversion is a line not through O.

2. Prove that two inverse points and the points in which the line determined by them intersect the circle of inversion form a harmonic set of points.

3. If two intersecting circles are each orthogonal to a third circle, show that their points of intersection are collinear with the center of the third circle.

4. If four harmonic points on a line L are inverted with respect to any point O of L distinct from each of the four points, prove that the inverse points form a harmonic set.

5. Show that, through two interior points A, B of circle (O) there is one and only one circle orthogonal to circle (O). *Hint:* Construct the inverse point A' to A with respect to circle (O), and show that the circle through A, A', B is orthogonal to circle (O).

6. Show that two orthogonal circles which intersect in two distinct points and are both orthogonal to a third circle C have one point of intersection inside and the other outside the third circle.

5.5. Angles Unchanged under Inversion

A property of inverse figures of prime importance in inversion theory is:

Theorem 5.7

The angle between any two curves intersecting at a point different from the center O of inversion is unchanged under inversion.

PROOF. Let the given curves C and D (Fig. 5.7) intersect in a point

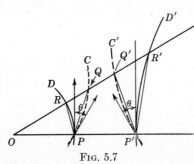

FIG. 5.7

P distinct from the center O of inversion, and let any line through O other than OP intersect these curves in the respective points R and Q. The inverse curves to C and D, C' and D', then intersect at the inverse point to P, P'. Furthermore, if curves C' and D' are met by line OR in the points Q' and R' inverse to the respective points Q and R, the theorem will be proved by showing that the angle θ between the tangents at P to curves C and D equals the angle θ' between the tangents at P' to curves C' and D'.

Since triangles OPQ and $OP'Q'$ are similar, as are triangles RPO and $R'P'O$,

$$\angle QPO = \angle OQ'P' \tag{1}$$

and
$$\angle RPO = \angle OR'P' \tag{2}$$

Hence, subtracting (2) from (1),

$$\angle QPR = \angle Q'P'R'$$

Now, as the line OQ rotates about O, the secant lines RP and PQ approach as limits the respective tangents at P to curves C and D. Similarly, the secant lines $Q'P'$ and $R'P'$ have as their limits the respective tangents at P' to curves C' and D'. Since angles QPR and $Q'P'R'$ are equal for every position of the rotating line, the limit angles θ and θ' are equal, and the theorem is proved.

Although inversion preserves the magnitudes of angles, it reverses their sense. In other words, as the ray PQ generates the angle QPR in a counterclockwise direction, its inverse ray $P'Q'$ generates the angle $Q'P'R'$ in the clockwise direction.

Since orthogonal circles intersect at a 90° angle and since tangent circles intersect at a 0° angle, the following statements are consequences of Theorem 5.7:

Corollary 1

Orthogonal circles invert into orthogonal circles.

Corollary 2

Tangent circles not through the center of inversion invert into tangent circles.

Corollary 3

Circles tangent to each other at the center of inversion invert into a system of parallel lines.

5.6. Peaucellier's Cell

Peaucellier's cell, the linkage which converts circular motion into rectilinear motion, will now be described. The cell consists of seven rigid rods. Four of them, each of length b, form a rhombus $APBP'$ (Fig. 5.8), and two others, each of length a, connect points A and B of the rhombus with a fixed point O. The figure is hinged at each of the five points A, P, B, P', O, and the seventh rod is used to connect point P with a fixed point C so determined that

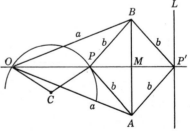

Fig. 5.8

$$PC = OC$$

In this way, point P is forced to move on an arc of a circle through O with its center at C.

It will now be shown that P and P' are inverse points with respect to a circle whose center is O. Since each of the points O, P, and P' are equidistant from points A and B, they lie on the perpendicular bisector of AB and are, therefore, collinear. Also, if M is the center of the rhombus $APBP'$,

$$OP \cdot OP' = (OM - PM)(OM + PM) = (OM)^2 - (PM)^2$$
$$= [(OM)^2 + (MB)^2] - [(PM)^2 + (MB)^2] = a^2 - b^2$$

Points P and P' are therefore inverse points with respect to the circle whose center is O and whose radius is $(a^2 - b^2)^{\frac{1}{2}}$. From Theorem 5.4 it then follows that, as point P describes a circle through O, its inverse point P' describes a straight line not through O. Peaucellier's cell thus converts circular motion into straight-line motion.

EXERCISES

1. If a circle is inverted into a circle, will the center of the first be the inverse of the center of the second? Prove your answer.

2. Construct the inverse of a given circle with respect to a center O of inversion when O is (a) outside the circle, (b) inside the circle, (c) on the circle.

3. Construct the inverse of circles A, B, C each tangent to line L at the center O of the circle of inversion.

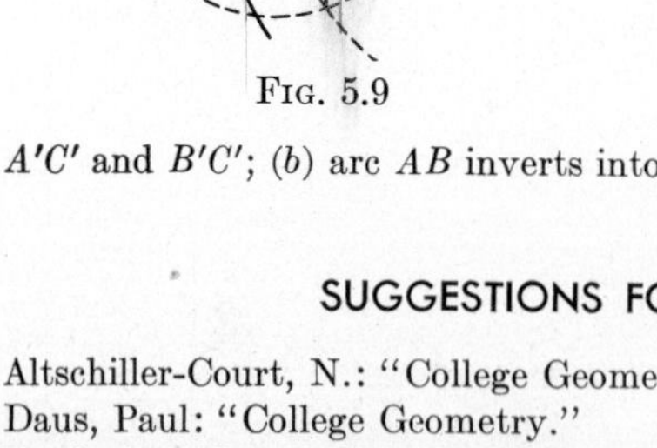

FIG. 5.9

4. If two circles are orthogonal, show that the inverse of the center of either circle with respect to the other circle is the mid-point of their common chord.

5. Let arcs AC, BC, and AB, each orthogonal to a fixed circle of center O, be inverted in a circle whose center R is the second point of intersection of the arcs AC and BC (Fig. 5.9). Show that (a) arcs AC and BC invert into straight lines $A'C'$ and $B'C'$; (b) arc AB inverts into an arc $A'B'$ of a circle.

SUGGESTIONS FOR FURTHER READING

Altschiller-Court, N.: "College Geometry."
Daus, Paul: "College Geometry."
Davis, David R.: "Modern College Geometry."
Johnson, R. A.: "Modern Geometry."
Shively, L. S.: "Modern Geometry."
Taylor, E. H., and G. C. Bartoo: "An Introduction to College Geometry."

Part Two

PROJECTIVE GEOMETRY

Chapter 6

PROJECTIONS, INVARIANTS, AND OTHER UNIFYING CONCEPTS

As so often happens in mathematics, it was a practical problem which gave the impetus needed for the formal development of projective geometry. The problem was literally forced on mathematicians by certain Renaissance artists, Leonardo da Vinci, Albrecht Dürer, and others, many of whom had noticed that, in the process of depicting people, objects, or scenes on canvas, considerable distortion takes place. Lengths, angles, areas, and other metric properties may be changed, and still the identity of the original is unmistakable. The questioning artists wanted to know why this was true. The answer was obvious: Identifying or distinguishing characteristics, now called *invariants*, were retained.

Some of these invariants are easily discernible. For example, straight lines in Fig. 6.1 are obviously pictures of straight lines, and a point of meeting of two lines is again a point of meeting of the transformed lines. Also points on a line go into points on another line. Thus concurrency of lines and collinearity of points are invariants.

On the other hand, angles seem to change; an obviously symmetrical octagonal plate is pictured as an octagon with unequal angles, and this change of angle is noted again in the checkerboard, where squares are transformed into parallelograms.

Other familiar objects are easily identified, although considerably distorted in the picture. Their invariants are more deeply hidden.

Analyze for a moment the method by which a picture is painted. As the artist looks at an object, rays of light enter his eye. When a transparent screen is placed between the eye and the object to be painted, these rays of light will meet the screen in a collection of points. It is this collection of points which the artist must draw if an observer is to receive the same impression from the painting as from the object itself.

FIG. 6.1. "Allegory of the Five Senses" by Baugin. (*Paris, Louvre*)

The television is one of the more recent ways for reproducing elements by purely mechanical methods. An artist, on the other hand, must perform the process either by artistic skill alone or by the use of some formal laws. What are these laws?

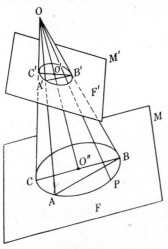

FIG. 6.2

The problem of the artist may be given a mathematical interpretation if physical concepts are replaced by their mathematical idealizations: the eye by a point O, the ray of light by a line, the screen by a plane M', and the object to be painted by a geometrical figure F lying in a plane M distinct from M' and not containing O.

Suppose the figure F consists of a circle and a line intersecting it in two points A, B (Fig. 6.2). Then, if each point of the figure is joined to the point O by straight lines, plane M' will cut each of these lines in a point.

The resulting collection of points is what the artist paints. It is called the image, or *projection*, of the original figure.

6.1. Projections and One-to-One (1-1) Correspondence

The projection process just described has established a correspondence between points P of a figure F and points P' of a second figure F' in such a way that to each point of one figure corresponds one and only one point of the other. *Such a correspondence is said to be one to one* (1-1).

The notion of a 1-1 correspondence is basic in practically all of mathematics and for that matter in everyday life. A child, for instance, learns to count by setting up a 1-1 correspondence between his fingers and the numbers 1, 2, . . . , 10.

A second familiar example of the usefulness of 1-1 correspondence is the seating arrangement in a class room. The correspondence is 1-1 when each student has a seat and each seat contains one and only one student. The 1-1 correspondence would be destroyed if there were a student without a seat or a seat without a student.

Another instance in which the correspondence fails to be 1-1 occurs in the Euclidean plane in connection with correspondences established between lines through a point P not on a line L and points A_i of L (Fig. 6.3). Each point A_i of L determines a line PA_i, but each line through P does not determine

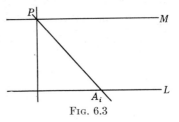

Fig. 6.3

a point A_i of L, for the line PM parallel to L fails to meet L in a corresponding point.

6.2. Perspectivities and Projective Transformations

It is customary to refer to the 1-1 correspondences established by a single projection as a *perspectivity,* reserving the name projective transformations to the correspondences established by a sequence of perspectivities. Thus, if figure F' of Fig. 6.2 is projected from a new center O' onto a third plane, a new figure F'' results which is in 1-1 correspondence with F' and hence with F. The 1-1 correspondence between F and F'' is then said to be a *projective correspondence, not a perspectivity.* Thus all perspectivities are projective correspondences, but not all projective correspondences are perspectivities.

6.3. Projective Properties

A study of the two figures F and F' of Fig. 6.2 reveals many of the invariants already noted in Fig. 6.1, as well as others. The projection

$A'B'$ of line segment AB is shorter than the original; the image of a circle is an ellipse; and the area of the ellipse is different from the area of the circle. Thus *distances, shape,* and *area* have changed; nevertheless many things have not changed. To each point P of F corresponds a point P' of F'; a straight line AB in F corresponds to a straight line $A'B'$ in F', for line AB and point O determine a plane which intersects plane M' in a line; intersecting lines AB and AP in the original are again intersecting lines in the image; points C, O'', B, on the same line, project into points C', O', B', which are also on a line. Thus it is seen again that collinearity of points and concurrency of lines are properties retained in the projection. They are called *projective properties*, in accordance with the definition:

A property of a figure which is preserved by every projection is a projective property.

It is with projective properties of figures that projective geometry is primarily concerned. In fact, the profound and intensive search for the more deeply hidden of these projective properties led to some of the most unusual and remarkable discoveries in the new field.

6.4. Rigid Motions. Metric Properties

The length of a line segment is not a projective property, but there is a transformation in which length is an invariant. It is the transformation of rigid motion, which, in a physical sense, is a movement of an object from one position in space to another, without in any way altering its shape or size. Such a transformation obviously preserves projective properties of figures such as collinearity of points and concurrency of lines, but it does much more. *It preserves all magnitudes.*

A property which is preserved by all rigid motions but not by every projection is, by definition, a metric property.

Distance, length, angle, and area are all metric notions, and theorems dealing with these concepts are called metric theorems. For example, the Pythagorean theorem (Theorem 47, Appendix A) is metric, and there are many others in elementary geometry.

Figures, too, are classified as *metric* or *projective*. For instance, a triangle is a projective figure, since a triangle projects into a triangle, assuming, of course, that the center of projection is not in the plane of the triangle. An equilateral triangle, on the other hand, may project into a triangle having unequal sides; this means that the equilateral property may be lost on projection. An equilateral triangle is, therefore, a metric, not a projective, figure.

Again, since some circles project into ellipses, the property of being a circle is not projective. However, the general conic is projective, since, as can be shown, a conic always projects into a conic.

EXERCISES

1. Which of the following figures are projective? Which are metric? (*a*) A parallelogram; (*b*) a triangle and its median; (*c*) a figure consisting of four points, no three of which are on a line, and the lines joining these points.

2. List five theorems of Appendix A which are not metric theorems.

6.5. Cross Ratio. Harmonic Points

In addition to those qualitative properties which are invariant under projection, there are certain quantitative properties which are also invariant. One of the most celebrated of these is the cross ratio of four points. It is now known, and has been proved, that the cross ratio (Secs. 4.5 and 10.8) of four elements (point or lines) is unaltered on projection. Thus, if the cross ratio of any four points in an original has the value λ and, in a supposedly final picture, photograph, or painting, has a value $\lambda' \neq \lambda$, cross ratio has not been preserved, and the authenticity of the reproduction is open to question, assuming, of course, that measuring instruments are sufficiently accurate.

Historically, cross ratio was a generalization of the notion of harmonic points, which were discovered originally by Apollonius about 220 B.C. and were studied later by De La Hire (1640–1718) from a projective viewpoint.

6.6. Other Unifying Concepts

About the beginning of the seventeenth century, there began to appear in the literature on geometry certain new concepts and unifying principles, among them continuity, infinitely distant elements, and the theory of imaginary, or complex, elements.

Continuity and infinitely distant points were introduced by Kepler (1571–1630), who, incidentally, recognized that ellipses, hyperbolas, and parabolas were not isolated curves but were all members of one family called conics. His ideas were further amplified by the well-known architect and engineer Gérard Desargues of Lyons (1593–1662).

Although Desargues failed to grasp the metric theory which results when infinite elements are used, his famous triangle theorem is frequently taken as a key in the development of a geometry free of metric concepts.

Pascal (1623–1662), a contemporary of Desargues and one of his ardent exponents, made many contributions to the classical field. His much-publicized theorem on the hexagon inscribed in a conic appealed so strongly to the imagination that it won wide popularity. From this theorem alone, Pascal obtained about four hundred corollaries. Had it not been for his early death, at the age of thirty-nine, he doubtless would have earned for himself a place among the immortals.

6.7. Modern Geometers

While Kepler, Desargues, Pascal, and others were making their discoveries in the realm of pure geometry, new developments were taking place in an entirely different direction. Geometry was being arithmetized. Complete justification of this process came in 1637 when Descartes published his "La Geometrie," which linked geometry with algebra and the number system and gave to the world the powerful tools needed for later developments.

Poncelet (1788–1867), a general in the French army under Napoleon, is indebted to this new system, called coordinate geometry, for some of his generalized views. Because a linear and a quadratic equation in two variables always have a solution in the field of complex numbers, and because these equations represent a line and a conic, respectively, Poncelet was led to the great unifying idea that a line and a conic have a point of intersection even when the coordinates of the point are not real. It was after he had been taken as a prisoner by the Russians, and while he was in prison at Saratov on the Volga (1813–1814) that Poncelet wrote his most famous work, "Traité des propriétés projectives des figures." This treatise and his later works justly earned for him the title "father of modern geometry."

Highlighting the developments of the eighteenth and nineteenth centuries were Gergonne's discovery (1826) of the very important principle of duality (Sec. 7.3) and the establishment of cross ratio as a fundamental quantitative invariant. Poncelet, Chasles, Brianchon, Dupin, Gergonne, and others emphasized the basic role of this famous invariant.

6.8. Nonmetric Developments

With the appearance of duality and cross ratio, projective geometry began to develop from a random collection of isolated theorems into a unified logical science. However, it was not until the publication of von Staudt's "Geometrie der Lage" (1847) and "Beitrage zur Geometrie der Lage" (1856) that the new science was seen to be independent of the notion of distance.

The idea of freeing geometry of metric concepts, an idea which came only after the discovery of non-Euclidean geometry, was a result of the search for a science which would include all geometries, thus unifying the entire field. Recognition of such a possibility came when it was found that the essential character of Euclidean and the basic non-Euclidean geometries was metric and that metric theorems differed in these various subfields.

The Englishman Arthur Cayley finally succeeded in showing that the Euclidean notion of distance could be defined in simple terms and was, in reality, only a particular case of a much more general projective definition. In 1859 he showed that both hyperbolic and elliptic non-Euclidean geometry could be defined as geometries associated with subgroups of the projective group. The proof emphasized the dominant role of projective geometry in the classification of geometries. Cayley's statement that "projective geometry is all geometry" is now classical.

Felix Klein later translated Cayley's algebraic methods into the language of pure geometry, and from that time on, projective geometry came to be recognized as the simplest type of geometry.

The invaluable contributions of Poncelet, Gergonne, von Staudt, Cayley, and Klein added to the works of other great mathematicians of the nineteenth and early twentieth centuries, such as those of Charles, Steiner, Reye, and Cremona, brought to a grand climax the early investigations in this all-important field. All of these men found in the new science a great aesthetic charm coupled with a most remarkable clarifying effect on geometry as a whole.

One final and important point is to be noted. In Cayley's projective definition of distance was found the solution of a number of problems in the ultramodern theory of special relativity. Once again, the mathematician had anticipated the needs of the scientist.

Chapter 7

BASIC AXIOMS, DUALITY, DESARGUES' THEOREM, AND PERSPECTIVE FIGURES

As stated previously, pure, or synthetic, projective geometry is not an extension of Euclidean geometry but is, rather, a perfectly logical system based on its own axioms concerning the undefined terms, point, line, and plane, and two undefined relations, incidence and separation. One subset of these axioms, incidence axioms, deals with the property of a point being on a line; and a second subset, existence axioms, deal with, as the name suggests, the actual existence of points and lines. These two sets of axioms will be listed and discussed first. After the axioms have been considered, a number of important consequences will be obtained. Desargues' theorem is one of them.

The point is stressed at the start of this formal development of projective geometry that the distance concept does not appear in this chapter or in the two following chapters. The material presented is strictly nonmetric theory; nevertheless its conclusions are many and far-reaching.

7.1. Incidence and Existence Axioms

Incidence Axioms

1. *If A and B are distinct points, there is at least one line on both A and B.*
2. *If A and B are distinct points, there is not more than one line on both A and B.*
3. *If A, B, C are points that are not all on the same line and if D, E are distinct points such that B, C, D are on a line and C, A, E are also on a line, there is a point F such that points A, B, F are on a line and points D, E, F are also on a line (Fig. 7.1).*

70

After a triangle has been defined, a substitute for Axiom 3 is:

3'. *If a line intersects two sides of a triangle, then it intersects the third side.*

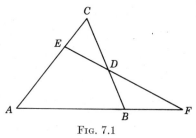

FIG. 7.1

Existence Axioms

4. *There exists at least one line.*
5. *There are at least three distinct points on every line.*
6. *Not all points are on the same line.*
7. *Not all points are on the same plane.*
8. *If S is a 3-space, every point is on S.*

Axioms 7 and 8 acquire meaning, of course, only after the plane and 3-space have been defined. To define the plane, Axioms 1, 2, and 6 are used to show the existence of two points A, B, of a unique line AB through these points, and of a third point D not on this line. A projective plane ABD is then, by definition, the totality of points on lines joining point D to points of the line AB.

By Axiom 7, there exists a point P not on the plane ABD, and by Axiom 5 at least one point on each of the lines joining P to points of the plane.

The totality of points joining P to points of the plane ABD is, by definition, a *projective 3-space*.

Projective *plane* geometries are obtained by replacing Axioms 7 and 8 by the single axiom:

7'. *If S_2 is a plane, every point is on S_2.*

The material of this text is confined, in the main, to projective geometry of the plane, and it is assumed in what follows that the plane satisfies at least Axioms 1 to 6.

7.2. Some Consequences of the Incidence and Existence Axioms

A few important results of the initial axioms are noted now. First, the axioms do not guarantee that a projective 3-space contains an infinite number of points. As a matter of fact, the axioms *can be* satis-fied by a projective 3-space containing only a finite number of points and lines [45, pp. 26–29]. Other axioms, needed to show that a line contains an infinite number of points, will be introduced later in the text.

The present axiomatic structure does suffice, however, for proofs of the following theorems:

Theorem 7.1

> *If two points of a line are on a given plane, every point of the line is on that plane.*

Theorem 7.2

> *Any two distinct lines of the plane intersect in a unique point.*

Theorem 7.3

> *A line and a plane in a 3-space must have at least one point in common.*

Theorem 7.4

> *Two distinct planes in a 3-space intersect in a line.*

Theorem 7.5

> *Three distinct planes in a 3-space have at least one point in common.*

The logical reasoning used in proofs of these theorems may be found in the literature [67, pp. 15–24]. Attention is being directed at this point, not to proofs, but to essential differences between Euclidean and projective theory, and one of these essential differences is seen in Theorem 7.2, which states that *two lines in the projective plane always meet.* In the *Euclidean plane,* two lines do not meet when they are parallel. *whereas in*

EXERCISE

Prove that, in any projective space satisfying Axioms 1 to 6, Sec. 7.1, every projective plane contains at least seven points.

7.3. Duality

Because two lines of the projective plane always meet, projective geometry possesses a distinctive characteristic not shared with the Euclidean system. It is the vitally important principle of duality, illustrated first in the two statements:

1. On two distinct *points* there is one and only one *line*.
2. On two distinct *lines* there is one and only one *point*.

Note that an interchange of the words "point" and "line" in one statement gives the other statement. When such is the case, either statement is called the dual of the other.

Another pair of dual statements are:

3. Three points not lying on the same line determine a plane.
4. Three planes not lying on the same line determine a point.

Here, it is an interchange of the words "point" and "plane" rather than "point" and "line" which accomplishes the transition from one statement to its dual, and in this case the dual statements represent duality, not in the plane, but in space.

Symmetry, or similarity, in both illustrations has been effected by the use of a peculiar terminology referred to as the "on" language. To say that a plane lies on a line may seem an awkward way of saying that a line lies on or in a plane, and to say that a line lies on a point may seem an equally strange way of saying that a line passes through a point, but such terminology makes the process of forming the dual of a given statement an automatic matter of interchanging the words "point" and "line" in one case and "point" and "plane" in the other.

Formal statements of the principle of duality, first for the plane and then for space, are as follows:

The Principle of Planar Duality

Any properly worded valid statement concerning incidence of points and lines in a projective plane gives rise to a second valid statement when the words "point" and "line" are interchanged.

The Principle of Space Duality

Any properly worded valid statement concerning incidence of points, lines, and planes in a projective 3-space gives rise to a second valid statement when the words "point" and "plane" are interchanged.

In this latter statement, the word "line" is left unchanged, since a line may be considered either as the join of two points or as the intersection (join) of two planes.

Both planar and space duality follow from the fact that, in a systematic development of projective geometry, axioms, definitions, and theorems are arranged in dual pairs. As a result, whenever a theorem is announced on the relative position of points and lines in a plane, or of points and planes in space, there is a dual theorem. If the original theorem is true, so is its dual, since proof of the original theorem consists in successive application of axioms, definitions, and theorems. Application of their duals, in turn, provides proof of the dual theorem. Logically, then, it is never necessary to prove the dual of a given theorem, once the theorem itself has been proved.

7.4. Dual Figures.   Complete Quadrilaterals and Quadrangles

In addition to dual theorems, in projective geometry there are dual operations and dual figures.   Dual to the operation of drawing a line through two points is that of extending two lines to meet in a point. Two lines through a point and two points on a line are known as dual figures.   More specifically, a figure consisting of a given number of lines and their points of intersection has for its dual a figure consisting of the same number of points and the lines determined by joining them in pairs.

The triangle is a mixed, or self-dual, figure, since it consists of three noncollinear points and the lines joining them in pairs or of three nonconcurrent lines and the points of meeting of pairs of these lines.

Two dual figures of importance in later developments are the *complete quadrilateral* and the *complete quadrangle*.

The *complete quadrilateral* consists of *four lines* in a plane, no three of which are concurrent, and the *six points* in which pairs of these lines intersect.   The lines are called *sides*, and the points, *vertices*.

Any two vertices which do not lie on the same side are *opposite vertices*, and a line joining a pair of opposite vertices is a *diagonal line* of the quadrilateral.

Since four *elements* may be grouped in pairs in three different ways, there are three diagonal lines in the complete quadrilateral.   If they do not all pass through the same point, these diagonals form the *diagonal triangle* of the quadrilateral.

Figure 7.2 shows a complete quadrilateral with sides, vertices, and diagonals as indicated below:

> 4 *sides:* a_1, a_2, a_3, a_4
> 6 *vertices:* (1,2), (1,3), (1,4), (2,3), (2,4), (3,4)
> 3 *diagonal lines:* d_1, d_2, d_3

In Euclidean geometry, the simple quadrilateral has four sides, like the complete quadrilateral of projective geometry, but only four vertices, not six, since two vertices are missing when both pairs of opposite sides are parallel.

The *complete quadrangle*, the dual of a complete quadrilateral, consists of *four points* in a plane, no three of which are collinear, and the *six lines* joining pairs of them.   The four points are the *vertices*, and the six lines are the *sides* of the quadrangle. A line joining two of the four points and the line joining the remaining points are called *opposite sides.* A point of intersection of opposite sides is called a *diagonal point*, and the three diagonal points, if they do not lie on a line, are the vertices of the diagonal triangle of the quadrangle.

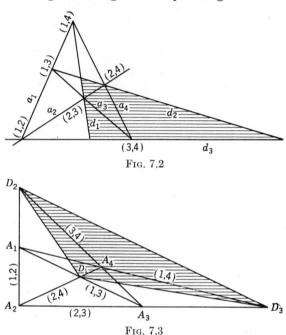

FIG. 7.2

FIG. 7.3

Figure 7.3 shows a complete quadrangle with vertices, sides, and diagonal points as indicated below:

4 *vertices:* A_1, A_2, A_3, A_4
6 *sides:* (1,2), (1,3), (1,4), (2,3), (2,4), (3,4)
3 *diagonal points:* D_1, D_2, D_3

7.5. The Quadrangle Axiom

When the points 1, 4, 7, 6 of Fig. 2.3 are taken as the vertices of a complete quadrangle, the points 2, 3, 5 are its diagonal points, and they lie on the (dotted) seventh line of the figure. But at that point we were considering a finite geometry in which a line contains only three points. A new axiom which rules out such a geometry is:

Axiom 9 (*The Quadrangle Axiom*)

The diagonal points of a complete quadrangle are not collinear.

With the aid of this new axiom, it is possible to prove that a line contains at least four points, but as yet the axiomatic structure is not sufficient to guarantee the existence of an infinite number of points on a line. It does suffice, however, for a proof of Desargues' famous triangle theorem, which is given in the next section.

EXERCISES

1. State (*a*) the plane dual and (*b*) the space dual of the theorem:

> *Any two distinct lines on the same plane determine a unique point.*

2. State the space dual of your answer to Exercise 1(*a*) above.

3. Fill in the blanks in the theorem on the right below and thus form the dual of the theorem on the left.

Theorem 7.6	*Theorem 7.7*
If two vertices of a variable triangle move on fixed lines while the sides pass through three fixed collinear points, the third vertex will likewise move on a fixed line.	*If two _____ of a variable triangle pass through fixed _____ while the _____ lie on three fixed _____, the third _____ will likewise pass through a fixed _____.*

4. Dualize the following theorem:

> *If three points A, C, D are chosen at random on a fixed line p and three points B, D, F at random on a fixed line q, the intersections of the lines AB with DE, BC with EF, CD with FA all lie on one straight line.*

5. Draw and describe the dual of each of the following: (*a*) a figure consisting of six lines *a*, *b*, *c*, *d*, *e*, *f* (Fig. 7.4) and four points *P*, *Q*, *R*, *S* such that on each point

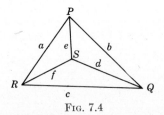

Fig. 7.4

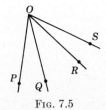

Fig. 7.5

are three of the given lines, and on each line lie two of the given points; (*b*) a figure consisting of four points *P*, *Q*, *R*, *S* (Fig. 7.5). On each point is a line, and all lines are on one point.

6. Given the diagonal triangle and one vertex of a quadrangle, show how to locate the remaining three vertices, using Axioms 1 to 3, Sec. 7.1. *Hint:* See [8, p. 15].

7. Prove that, in a geometry based on the eight axioms of Sec. 7.1 and the quadrangle axiom just given, a line contains at least four points. *Hint:* See [45, p. 55].

7.6. Desargues' Theorem

So far, nine axioms of projective geometry have been introduced, but nowhere has there been any mention of distance, nor has any use been made of number concepts and algebra.   Parallel lines are missing, and so are perpendicular ones.   Yet, in many respects the geometry resembles the familiar one of high school days, and one might reasonably ask what has been gained by this new approach.   Desargues' famous triangle theorem will provide a partial answer to this question.

The proof of this theorem given in Sec. 3.6 uses metric concepts, which are really superfluous.   Stripping a proof of its metric covering, as will be done, is like clearing the forest of the underbrush which hides treasures underneath.   Desargues' theorem holds in a simpler geometry than Euclid's.

Theorem 7.8 (Desargues' Theorem)

> *If two triangles are so situated that the lines joining pairs of corresponding vertices are concurrent, the pairs of corresponding sides will intersect in three collinear points, and conversely.*

PROOF.   The theorem is proved easily when the two triangles are in different planes, one triangle, say $A_2B_2C_2$, in the base of a triangular pyramid and the other in a plane cutting the pyramid in the triangle $A_1B_1C_1$ (Fig. 7.6). Let the lines A_1A_2, B_1B_2, and C_1C_2 joining pairs of corresponding vertices meet in the vertex O of the pyramid.   The lines A_1B_1 and A_2B_2 lying in the same plane intersect in a point, say C'. Similarly, lines B_1C_1 and B_2C_2 meet at a point A', and lines A_1C_1 and A_2C_2 at a point B'.   The points A', B', C' therefore lie in the plane of the tri-

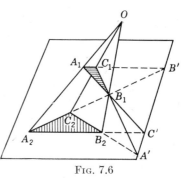

FIG. 7.6

angle $A_1B_1C_1$ and also in the plane of triangle $A_2B_2C_2$.   By Theorem 7.4, these planes intersect in a line, and thus the theorem is proved when the triangles are in different planes.

The proof when the two triangles are in the same plane is considerably more complicated.   It can be reduced to the one just given.   To do this, let P be the plane of the given triangles $A_1B_1C_1$ and $A_2B_2C_2$ (Fig. 7.7), and let these triangles be perspective (see Sec. 7.7) from point O.   Also, let a_i, b_i, c_i be the sides opposite the respective vertices A_i, B_i, C_i, of these triangles, where $i = 1, 2$.   Choose any two points S_1 and S_2 collinear with O, both points being outside the plane P of the triangles.

Since the lines A_1A_2 and S_1S_2 intersect at point O, the lines S_1A_1 and S_2A_2 are coplanar and hence intersect at a point A. Similarly, the lines S_1B_1 and S_2B_2 intersect at a point B, and the lines S_1C_1 and S_2C_2 at a point C. Let P' be the plane of the triangle whose vertices are the points A, B, C, and let a, b, c be sides opposite the respective vertices A, B, C.

Triangles $A_1B_1C_1$ and ABC are in the distinct planes P and P', and, by the case just proved, corresponding sides a_1 and a, b_1 and b, c_1 and c meet in the respective points A'', B'', C'' on the line L of intersection of these two planes P and P'.

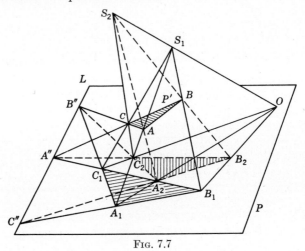

FIG. 7.7

Similarly, the triangles A_2B_2C and ABC have corresponding sides a_2, a; b_2, b; c_2, c, which meet in points of this same line L. But—and here is the key to the argument—there is only one point C'' in which line AB and hence lines A_1B_1 and A_2B_2 meet L. Similarly, AC meets L at the point B'' of meeting of lines A_1C_1 and A_2C_2, and BC meets line L at the point A'' of meeting of lines B_1C_1 and B_2C_2. The points A'', B'', C'' of meeting of corresponding sides in the two triangles therefore lie on a line L. The theorem is therefore proved when the triangles lie in the same plane and when the lines joining corresponding vertices are distinct.

Such a proof makes use of points outside the plane of the triangle. The theorem cannot be proved using only Axioms 1 to 6, Sec. 7.1, and the additional assumption that all points are in the same plane (see Sec. 9.5).

Geometries for which Desargues' theorem does not hold are called non-Desarguesian geometries. A discussion of these systems may be found in the literature [52, Chap. 8, pp. 124–128].

Although it may happen that a vertex of one triangle lies on a side of the other, or that the triangles may be further specialized, the accompanying complications are not serious and may be left as exercises.

The converse of Desargues' theorem does not require a separate proof, once the principle of duality has been accepted, for the converse is simply the dual of the original.

7.7. Perspective Triangles

When two triangles, as $A_1B_1C_1$ and $A_2B_2C_2$ (Fig. 7.7), are so situated that lines joining pairs of corresponding vertices are concurrent at a point O, the triangles are said to be *perspective,* and the line containing the points of meeting of corresponding sides is called the axis of perspectivity of the two triangles.

This definition of perspective triangles may be extended to polygons of more than three sides. Thus, if in two polygons $A_1A_2 \ldots A_n$ and $B_1B_2 \ldots B_n$, the lines A_iB_i, $i = 1, \ldots, n$ are concurrent at a point O, the polygons are perspective.

Remark

In drawing two perspective triangles, an artist probably knows from experience that the three points of meeting of pairs of corresponding sides will fall on the same line. If he has mastered Desargues' theorem, he will have the mathematician's answer to one of his early questions: "Why do these three points lie on a line?"

7.8. Perspective Quadrangles and Quadrilaterals

A first important application of Desargues' theorem is given in the following theorem:

Theorem 7.9

If two complete quadrangles are so situated that five pairs of corresponding sides intersect in points of one straight line, then the sixth pair of corresponding sides will intersect in a point of the same line.

PROOF. In the quadrangles $ABCD$ and $A'B'C'D'$ (Fig. 7.8), let P, Q, R, S, T be the five points of intersection of pairs of corresponding sides AD and $A'D'$, BC and $B'C'$, BD and $B'D'$, DC and $D'C'$, AB and $A'B'$. and let these five points lie on a line L. The theorem will then be proved by showing that the sixth pair of corresponding sides AC and $A'C'$ also meet in a point of this same line.

Since the triangles BCD and $B'C'D'$ have line L as an axis of perspectivity, it follows from Desargues' theorem that the lines BB', CC', and DD' are concurrent at a point, say O.

But the triangles ABD and $A'B'D'$ also have line L as an axis of perspectivity; hence they are also perspective. This means, since the lines BB' and CC' are already known to meet at point O, that line AA' also passes through O and hence that the triangles ABC and $A'B'C'$

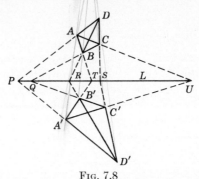

Fig. 7.8

are perspective from this point. Since line L is the axis of perspectivity of these latter triangles, the lines AC and $A'C'$ intersect in a point U of line L, and Theorem 7.9 is proved.

From the principle of duality follows the dual theorem:

Theorem 7.10

If two complete quadrilaterals are so situated that five of the lines joining pairs of corresponding vertices pass through one point, the lines joining the sixth pair of corresponding vertices will pass through the same point.

EXERCISES

1. Prove each of the following theorems:

(a) *If three triangles have a common center of perspective, their three axes of perspectivity are concurrent.*

(b) *If three triangles are perspective in pairs and if the pairs have a common axis of perspective, the centers of perspective are collinear.*

(c) *If, in the triangles ABC and $A'B'C'$, the lines AA', BB', CC' are concurrent, the six points of intersection of the pairs of lines AB, $A'B'$; BC, $B'C'$; CA, $C'A'$; $A'B$, AB'; $C'B$, BC'; $C'A$, CA' lie by threes on four straight lines.*

2. Show that the diagonal triangle of a quadrangle is perspective with each of the four triangles formed by a set of three of the vertices of the quadrangle, the center of perspectivity being in each case the fourth vertex.

3. Prove Theorem 7.10 without using the principle of duality.

Concluding Remarks

The entire theory of this chapter has been based on only two sets of axioms, the incidence and existence axioms given in Sec. 7.1; through their use a number of basic facts have been established. Among other things, Desargues' famous theorem has been proved without the use of the metric concepts which entered into the earlier proof of Sec. 3.6. It is indeed surprising how much significant theory can be developed before distance is needed, or used.

In the next chapter, another set of axioms will be introduced and their consequences studied. By the time the final set of axioms used in this development have been presented, a considerable body of theory will be at hand. Building or creating a new geometry is much like other construction projects: The superstructure is built only after the foundation has been carefully laid.

Chapter 8

PROJECTIVE THEORY OF HARMONIC ELEMENTS. ADDITIONAL AXIOMS

Theorems 7.9 and 7.10 will now be used to give purely *projective* definitions of harmonic elements, in contrast with the earlier definitions of Sec. 4.1 which involved *metric* concepts. As in the case of Desargues' theorem, these metric concepts are superfluous and tend to disguise the simplicity of the harmonic concept as well as its projective nature.

After the new definitions have been given, there will be added to the present axiomatic structure another set of assumptions called *separation axioms*. These new axioms, which, incidentally, take the place of order axioms in Euclid, will be used to show that a line contains an infinite number of points. Only one final axiom will then be needed to show that points of a line may be put into 1-1 correspondence with elements of a number system. This is the preparation, among other things, for the material of Chaps. 10 and 11, where coordinate geometry and transformation theory are discussed.

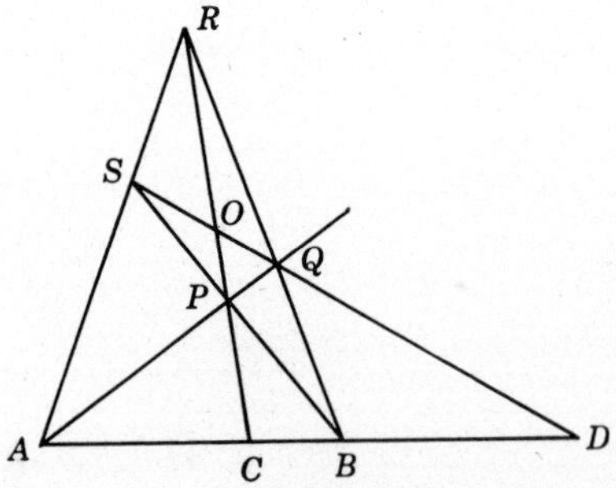

Fig. 8.1

8.1. Projective Definition of Harmonic Points

It was shown in Fig. 7.8 that a line not through a vertex of a quadrangle meets the six sides of the quadrangle in six points, which may or may not all be distinct. As a matter of fact, special interest is attached to the case when they are not all distinct, as in the quadrangle $PQRS$ of Fig. 8.1, where the line through two of the diagonal points A and B of the quadrangle passes through the points C and D

82

in which sides through the remaining diagonal point meet this line. These four points A, B, C, D are called *harmonic*, in accordance with the formal definition:

> *Four points on a straight line are, by definition, harmonic when they are so related that two of them are diagonal points of a quadrangle, while the remaining two are the points in which the sides passing through the third diagonal point meet the line joining these two diagonal points.*

Other definitions are the same as those already given in Sec. 4.1. Thus the points C, D of Fig. 8.1 are harmonic conjugates with respect to points A and B, and D (or C) is called the *harmonic conjugate* of C (or D) with respect to the points A and B. The symbol $H(AB,CD)$ denotes that pairing of the harmonic points in which points C, D are harmonic conjugates of A, B.

8.2. Harmonic Conjugates

The projective definition of harmonic points is a far cry from the earlier metric one of Sec. 4.1, but certain similarities appear on closer observation. The new, as well as the old, definition automatically separates the four points into pairs, two diagonal points forming elements of one pair while the remaining points are elements of the other pair. Also, by Theorem 7.9, point D of the harmonic set $H(AB,CD)$ is uniquely determined as soon as points A, B, and C are given. This fact is stated formally in the next theorem:

Theorem 8.1

> *The harmonic conjugate of a point with respect to two others is uniquely determined.*

Furthermore, if C, D are harmonic with respect to A and B, then A, B are harmonic with respect to C and D.

To prove this statement, let the harmonic set $H(AB,CD)$ of Fig. 8.2 be determined by the quadrangle $PQRS$ with diagonal points at A and B. It will then be shown that C and D are diagonal points of another quadrangle with its remaining two sides passing through A and B.

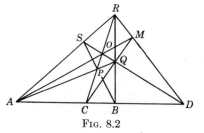

FIG. 8.2

Draw CQ and DR intersecting at M, and let O be the intersection of lines PR and QS, as indicated by the symbol

$$\binom{PR}{QS} = O$$

Then in the triangles POS and RQM of Fig. 8.2

$$\binom{SO}{RM} = D \qquad \binom{PO}{QM} = C \qquad \binom{SP}{RQ} = B$$

The triangles POS and RQM are therefore perspective from line BD, and from Desargues' theorem the line OM passes through A. Hence in the quadrangle $OQMR$, points C, D are *diagonal* points while A and B are on the remaining sides of the quadrangle. Thus proof has been given of the following theorem:

Theorem 8.2

If points C, D are harmonic with respect to points A and B, then points A, B are harmonic with respect to points C and D.

8.3. Harmonic Lines

The plane dual of a harmonic set of points is a harmonic set of lines. Thus,

Four lines on a point are, by definition, harmonic when they are so related that two of them are diagonal sides of a quadrilateral while the remaining two are lines joining the point of meeting of these two diagonals to the remaining two vertices.

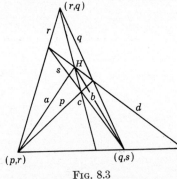

For example, in the quadrilateral p, q, r, s (Fig. 8.3) H is the point of meeting of the two diagonals c and d, while a and b are the lines joining point H to the points (p,r) and (q,s). The lines a, b, c, d through point H are harmonic. The lines c, d are harmonic conjugates of the lines a, b; c (or d) is called the harmonic conjugate of d (or c) with respect to the lines a and b.

Fig. 8.3

The duality principle applied to Theorems 8.1 and 8.2 gives two more theorems.

Theorem 8.3

The harmonic conjugate of a line with respect to two other lines is uniquely determined.

Theorem 8.4

> *If lines a, b are harmonic with respect to lines c, d, then lines c, d are harmonic with respect to lines a, b.*

8.4. The Invariance of the Harmonic Property on Projection

The great importance of the harmonic property lies in the fact that this property is retained on projection. For points in the Euclidean plane, the property was stated formally in Theorem 4.4. In the projective plane, there is not only this theorem but its dual theorem as well.

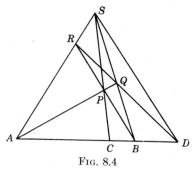

As a preparation for the dual theorem, let points A,B and C,D (Fig. 8.4) form a harmonic set $H(AB,CD)$ of points and let S be any point not on the line of these points.

Fig. 8.4

It will then be shown that lines SA, SB and SC, SD through the point S form a harmonic set of lines.

Draw a line through A meeting SC and SB in points P and Q, respectively. Also, draw a line BP meeting SA in R. The quadrangle $SRPQ$ has diagonal points at A and B and one of its sides passes through C. By Theorem 7.9 the sixth side RQ passes through the point D.

On the other hand, the lines AD, AQ and RD, RB form a quadrilateral of which SA and SB are diagonals while SC and SD pass through the remaining two vertices. From the definition of harmonic lines, the lines SA, SB and SC, SD are harmonic, and the following theorem is proved.

Theorem 8.5

> *The lines joining a harmonic set of points to a point not on the line of the points is a harmonic set of lines.*

From the principle of duality follows the dual theorem:

Theorem 8.6

> *The points of meeting of a harmonic set of lines with a line not through their point of meeting is a harmonic set of points.*

Another way of stating this theorem is:

> *A line not through a vertex of a harmonic set of lines intersects these lines in a harmonic set of points.*

8.5. Separation Axioms

A distinction is to be made now between the projective and the Euclidean lines. It is linked with the common notion of "separation," illustrated many times in everyday life in such cases as a wall separating one room of a house from another, two countries being separated by a mountain range, a piece of string being separated into parts by a single cut, or a circular wire being separated into two parts by two cuts.

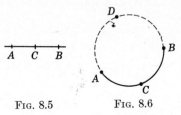

FIG. 8.5   FIG. 8.6

On the Euclidean line, a single point C separates a point A from a point B (Fig. 8.5) in the sense that, starting at either point and moving continuously in the same direction, one encounters the point C. The situation is quite different, however, if the three points are situated on a circle (Fig. 8.6), where the points A and B are extremities of two different segments, one being the heavy line segment, the other, the dotted line segment.

If C is a point on one of these segments, say the heavy line of Fig. 8.6, one can move from A to B on the dotted segment without encountering C. But, if there is a point D located on this dotted segment, one cannot move from A to B in either direction without encountering one or the other of these points C and D. That is why *two* points rather than a *single* one are needed to separate two points on a circle. The symbol

$$AB//CD$$

is used to denote the separation of the pair of points A, B by the pair C, D.

What can be said about the relative positions of the points A, B, C of the harmonic set $H(AB,CD)$ of Fig. 8.1? Does C separate the point A from the point B? If you say yes, you are in error, and presently you will see why.

Suppose A, B, C are three fixed points on a line of the projective plane. Starting with these three points, one can construct a series of sets of harmonic points:

$$H(AB,CD_1) \qquad H(AD_1,BD_2) \qquad H(AD_2,D_1D_3) \cdots$$
$$H(AD_{n-1},D_{n-2}D_n)$$

(see Fig. 8.7), and another question arises. Are the points D_1, D_2, ..., D_n distinct? This question cannot be answered in the affirmative without the aid of new axioms dealing with an undefined relation called "separation." These axioms, which constitute additions to our basic axiomatic structure for projective geometry and hence are numbered in sequence with the earlier axioms of Secs. 7.1 and 7.5, are presented below.

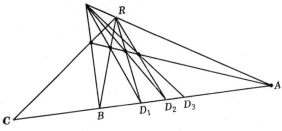

FIG. 8.7

Separation Axioms

10. *The pairs of a harmonic set of points* $H(AB,CD)$ *separate each other.*

11. *If the pairs of points* A, B *and* C, D *separate each other and if the pairs* A, D_1 *and* D_2, B *separate each other, then the pairs* A, B *and* C, D_2 *separate each other.*

12. *If the pairs* A, B *and* C, D *separate each other, then* A, B, C, D *are distinct points.*

Now that the separation axioms have been given and the symbol $AB//CD$ explained, a segment of the projective line may be defined.

If A, B, C *are three points of the line* L, *the segment* AB *is the set of points* X *for which* $AB//CX$.

By means of a somewhat lengthy proof, it is possible to prove that two distinct points A, B of the projective line are extremities of two different segments, just as if the two points were on a circle. The proof, which is omitted, may be found in the literature [18, Sec. 3.31].

8.6. The Net of Rationality

The sequence of points D_1, D_2, . . . , D_n of Fig. 8.7 was obtained by starting with three fixed points A, B, C of a line and constructing a series of harmonic points:

$$H(AB,CD_1) \qquad H(AD_1,BD_2) \; \cdots \; H(AD_{n-1},D_{n-2}D_n)$$

Two useful definitions concerning such a set of points are:

A point X *of the line* L *is said to be harmonically related to three distinct points* A, B, C *of the line if* X *is one point of a sequence of points*

A, B, C, D_1, D_2, . . . , $D_n(=X)$ *such that D_1 is the harmonic conjugate of one of the points A, B, C with respect to the other two, and such that any following point D_j is the harmonic conjugate of any one of the preceding points of the sequence with respect to two other preceding points of the sequence.*

The set of all points on a line harmonically related to three given distinct points A, B, C of the line is called the net of rationality determined by the points A, B, C.

It is possible to show (see Exercise 3 below) that points of the net of rationality are infinite in number, and hence that the projective line contains an infinite number of points.

EXERCISES

In the following exercises, A, B, C are three fixed points of a line L.

1. If D_1 is a point such that $H(AB,CD_1)$, is D_1 distinct from points A, B, C? Prove your answer.

2. If D_2 is a point of L such that $H(AD_1,BD_2)$, is D_2 distinct from D_1 and C? Why?

3. If D_1, D_2, . . . , D_n is a sequence of points such that $H(AB,CD_1)$, $H(AD_1,BD_2)$, . . . , $H(AD_{n-1},D_{n-2}D_n)$, prove that D_n is distinct from D_b for all positive integers such that $b < n$.　*Hint:* See [45, p. 81].

8.7. The Continuity Axiom

Thus far, the axiomatic structure, consisting of 12 assumptions, including the separation axioms, has guaranteed the existence of an infinite number of points on a line. They were points of a net of rationality determined by three fixed points.

One final axiom, the continuity axiom, is still needed to provide for the existence of still other points on the line.

Various ways of stating this axiom may be found in the literature. One statement is as follows:

Axiom 13 (*The Continuity Axiom*)

For every partition of all the points of a segment into two nonvacuous sets, such that no point of either set lies between two points of the other, there is a point of one set which lies between every other point of that set and every point of the other set.

Because of this axiom it is possible to set up a 1-1 correspondence between points of the projective line and numbers of an abstract number system, of which the two most familiar examples are the real and the complex number systems.

A number x thus associated with a point P of the line is called its coordinate, and the point is then indicated $P(x)$.

When the number system employed in the process is real (complex), the point $P(x)$ is said to be real (complex), and the point associated with the symbol ∞ is called the ideal point $P(\infty)$ of the line.

The method is a familiar one in elementary coordinate geometry, where the number associated with a point of the line is usually its distance from a fixed point of the line. In a similar way, starting with three fixed points of the projective line, denoted $P(0)$, $P(1)$, and $P(\infty)$, a real number x may be attached to each point of the projective line. Details of the process are lengthy and are best left for more advanced and detailed discussions [46, Chap. 7; 76, Chap. 8].

More will be written in Chap. 10 of coordinates and their use in geometry.

8.8. Constructions in Projective Geometry

In elementary geometry, a construction problem involves an explanation of how the straightedge and compasses may be used to obtain new points and lines, which may in turn determine other desired points or lines.

The classical restrictions to these two instruments were apparently suggested by the following three of Euclid's axioms:

1. A straight line may be drawn from any point to any point.
2. A finite straight line may be produced continuously in a straight line.
3. A circle may be drawn with any center and any radius.

Constructions made in accordance with these axioms are called ruler-and-compass constructions. By the ruler is here meant an unmarked straightedge. The modern ruler is a graded straightedge.

As Euclid's axioms have been interpreted, they place restrictions not only on the instruments to be used in the construction but also on the manner in which they are to be used. The straightedge is to be used for drawing a line through two given points and extending it in either direction. That is all.

The third axiom tells how the compasses are to be used. When Euclid drew his circles, probably on the sand, the center had to be given and a point on the circumference. Then it was as if the compasses automatically closed, so that this same position of the compasses could not be used to draw another circle. However, Euclid's second axiom shows how to construct at any given point a line segment equal to a given line segment. Circles were then drawn by using a radius equal to a given line segment.

With the straightedge and compasses, the ancient Greeks were able to solve a variety of problems. They bisected lines and angles, drew perpendiculars to lines, erected tangents to circles, and constructed certain regular polygons. They even disposed of the famous problem of Apollonius (about 250 B.C.), in which three arbitrary circles in the plane are given and a fourth circle tangent to all three is required.

In the present treatment of projective geometry, in which distance has not been defined, the compasses can have no part in construction problems, but it is an interesting observation that many of the straight-edge-ruler-compass constructions of elementary geometry may be replaced by constructions using only a straightedge. One such construction is given for the following problem:

Construction Problem I

When three points A, B, C of a harmonic set of points are given, construct the fourth point D harmonic to C with respect to A and B.

To perform the construction, draw through any one of the given points, say A, any two lines, and let a line through a second given point C meet these lines in the points P and R (Fig. 8.1). Connect the third given point B with P and R, and let lines BP and BR meet lines AR and AP in the respective points S and Q. Then, line QS meets line AB in the desired point D. The proof of the construction follows immediately from the definition of harmonic points (Sec. 8.1).

The next problem is a particularly challenging one.

Construction Problem II

Given a line segment AB and a domain W in a plane m, construct the extension of AB, using only a straightedge, so that the straightedge never crosses W during the construction.

To perform the construction, choose an arbitrary point C on the line segment AB (Fig. 8.8), and construct two quadrangles $P_1Q_1R_1S_1$ and $P_2Q_2R_2S_2$, one above AB and the other below AB. The lines S_1Q_1 and S_2Q_2 then intersect in a point D of the line AB.

Repeat the process for a second point C' of the line segment AB, thereby obtaining the harmonic conjugate D' of point C'. The line DD' is the required extension of AB. (Why?)

The separation axioms of Sec. 8.5 are needed to show that, if C and C' are points on one of the segments determined by points A and B, then D and D' are on the other segment determined by these same two points.

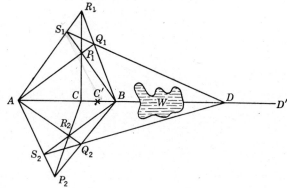

FIG. 8.8

Concluding Remarks

The present development of projective geometry has been based on three incidence axioms and five existence axioms (Sec. 7.1), the quadrangle axiom (Sec. 7.5), the separation axioms (Sec. 8.5), and the continuity axiom (Sec. 8.7). The last axiom was used to associate a coordinate number x of a number system with points of the line, and it is now possible to introduce coordinates and algebraic methods into geometry. Before this is done, however, some final facts about perspectivities and projectivities will be presented and used in a new, nonmetric approach to the theory of conics.

These new facts will illustrate some of the many beautiful and far-reaching conclusions deduced from the present axiomatic structure.

EXERCISES

1. Can a 1-1 correspondence be established between points of the Euclidean line and points of the projective line? Give reasons for your answer. *Hint:* Let P of Fig. 8.9 be a point not on the projective line L. Then a 1-1 correspondence exists between lines through P and points A of L. If the same figure represents a Euclidean plane in which PM is parallel to L, what point of L corresponds to this parallel?

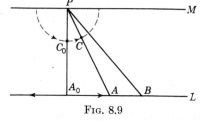

FIG. 8.9

2. Can you determine in a drawing the harmonic conjugate D of point $C(1)$ with respect to points $A(0)$, $B(2)$ of line L of the Euclidean plane if the coordinate of a point represents its distance from a fixed point of the plane? Why?

3. Construct three points of a harmonic net determined by three given points of a line.

4. If A, B, C are three given collinear points, how may a point P be determined with straightedge alone so that line CP passes through points A and B?

Chapter 9

PERSPECTIVITIES, PROJECTIVITIES, AND THE PROJECTIVE THEORY OF CONICS

Points on a line, called a pencil of points, and the coplanar lines through a point, called a pencil of lines, are known as one-dimensional forms, since they each consist of a single infinity of elements. Perspectivities between them are discussed next.

9.1. Perspectivities

It will be recalled that a correspondence between two pencils of points is a perspectivity if the lines joining pairs of corresponding points are *concurrent*. Dually, a correspondence between two pencils of lines is a perspectivity if the points of intersection of pairs of corresponding lines are *collinear*.

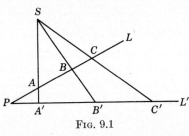

FIG. 9.1

The symbol for a perspectivity is $\overline{\underset{\wedge}{}}$. Thus

$$A, B, C, \ldots \overline{\underset{\wedge}{S}} A', B', C', \ldots$$

means that points $A, B, C, \ldots$ of a line L (Fig. 9.1) are perspective through point S with points A', $B', C', \ldots$ of a second line L' in such a way that A corresponds to A', B to B', C to C', . . . , and so that the lines AA', BB', CC', . . . are concurrent at S. The point S is called the center of the perspectivity. The point P of meeting of lines L and L' is a self-corresponding point in that point P of line L corresponds to point P of line L', and vice versa.

Dually,

$$a, b, c, \ldots \overline{\underset{\wedge}{s}} a', b', c', \ldots$$

means that the pencil of rays $a, b, c, \ldots$ (Fig. 9.2) is perspective with the pencil of rays a', b', c', . . . so that ray a corresponds to a', b to b', c to c', . . . , and so that the points of meeting of corresponding rays are on the same line s, called the axis of the perspectivity.

If S and S' are the centers of the two pencils of Fig. 9.2, the common ray SS' is a self-corresponding ray in that SS' may be considered a ray of either the pencil with S as a center or the pencil of rays with S' as a center.

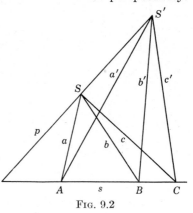

Fig. 9.2

Perspectivities may exist between forms of different kinds in accordance with the definition:

A pencil of points and a pencil of lines are perspective if the points are on a transversal of the pencil of lines and if each point corresponds to the line on which it lies.

EXERCISE

Given a triangle ABC and two distinct points A', B', determine a point C' such that the lines AA', BB', CC' are concurrent in a point O and the lines AB', BC', CA' are concurrent in a point O', distinct from O. (The two triangles are then said to be doubly perspective.)

9.2. Projectivities

A discussion of projectivities begins with the formal definition:

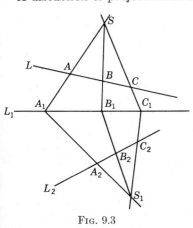

Fig. 9.3

A correspondence between elements of two one-dimensional forms is a projectivity if such a correspondence is made by a finite sequence of perspectivities.

A projectivity is illustrated in Fig. 9.3, where points A, B, C, . . . of line L are perspective through a point S with points A_1, B_1, C_1, . . . of a second line L_1, and the points of L_1 are in turn perspective through another center S_1 with the points A_2, B_2, C_2, . . . of a third line L_2. Then, every point of L corresponds to a uniquely determined point of L_2: A to A_2, B to B_2, C to C_2, . . . , and this correspondence between points of L and points of L_2 is a *projectivity*, denoted by the symbol $\overline{\wedge}$. Thus

$$A, B, C, \ldots \ \overline{\wedge} \ A_2, B_2, C_2, \ldots$$

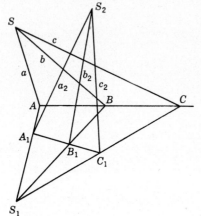

means that points $A, B, C, \ldots$ are projective with points $A_2, B_2, C_2,$ $\ldots$ in such a way that A corresponds to A_2, B to B_2, C to C_2, $\ldots$. Dually,

$$a, b, c, \ldots \ \overline{\wedge} \ a_2, b_2, c_2, \ldots$$

means that lines $a, b, c, \ldots$ and $a_2, b_2, c_2, \ldots$ are projective in such a way that a corresponds to a_2, b to b_2, c to c_2, $\ldots$ (Fig. 9.4).

9.3. A Basic Theorem

It would seem at first glance as if the number of perspectivities necessary to effect a projectivity would depend on the particular problem

Fig. 9.4

at hand, but such is not the case as the following, quite surprising theorem, shows:

Theorem 9.1

If A, B, C are three points of a line L and A', B', C', are three points of another line L', where L and L' are in the same plane, then the points A, B, C can be projectively related to points A', B', C' by at most two centers of perspectivity.

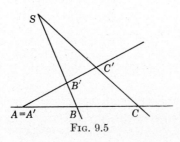

Fig. 9.5

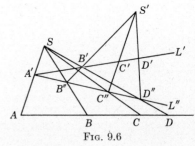

Fig. 9.6

The proof, in case a point, say A, coincides with its corresponding point A' (Fig. 9.5), is simple, for then the single center S of intersection of the lines BB' and CC' suffices for the desired projectivity.

If no two corresponding points coincide (Fig. 9.6), a point S on a line joining a pair of corresponding points, say A and A', may be chosen as *one* center of perspectivity, and a line L'' drawn through point A'. If the lines SB and SC meet L'' in the respective points B'' and C'', the point S' of meeting of the lines $B''B'$ and $C''C'$ is the *second* center which effects the desired projectivity, for

$$A, B, C \stackrel{S}{\barwedge} A', B'', C'' \stackrel{S'}{\barwedge} A', B', C'$$

and hence

$$A, B, C \barwedge A', B', C'$$

The argument is still valid if one of the points, say A, coincides with a point B', other than its corresponding one (see Exercise 1, page 97).

Corollary

If A, B, C and A', B', C' are on the same line, three centers of perspectivity are sufficient to project the three points A, B, C into the points A', B', C'.

If points A, B, C of line L are projected through point S into the points A'', B'', C'' of a line L'' distinct from L, then by the theorem just proved, two more centers are required to effect a projectivity between these latter points and the new points A', B', C'. Thus, in all, three centers of perspectivity are needed to project points A, B, C of a line into points A', B', C' of the same line.

9.4. The Fundamental Theorem of Projective Geometry

If now a fourth point D is selected on line AB (Fig. 9.6), its corresponding point D' of line L' is automatically determined by the projectivity which related points A, B, C to points A', B', C', and a natural question to investigate now is whether or not a different choice for the intermediate line L'' would determine a corresponding point on L' different from D'. In other words, is a projectivity completely determined when three pairs of corresponding elements are given?

A preparatory theorem needed to answer this question is the following:

Theorem 9.2

A projective transformation between the points of a given line which leaves three distinct points of the line fixed, leaves fixed every point of the line.

A rigorous detailed proof of this theorem is properly left for more extensive and advanced investigations than are being given here. A summary of the arguments follows.

The proof makes use of the facts that a projective transformation is continuous and that points of a net of rationality are everywhere dense, i.e., on any segment determined by two distinct points A, B of such a net, there exist points of the net.

Now, a projective transformation which leaves the three distinct points A, B, C fixed obviously leaves fixed every point of the net of rationality determined by A, B, C. But the transformation which leaves fixed every point of the net of rationality also leaves fixed every point of a set of points everywhere dense on the line and, the transformation being continuous, leaves fixed every point on the line.

The next theorem is usually referred to as the fundamental theorem of projective geometry.

Theorem 9.3

A projectivity between two one-dimensional forms is completely determined by three distinct pairs of corresponding elements.

The theorem will be proved for two pencils of points in which the distinct points A, B, C of one pencil correspond to points A', B', C' of the other. If, then, in one sequence of perspectivities A, B, C, $D \overline{\wedge} A'$, B', C', D' and if in another sequence of perspectivities A, B, C, $D \overline{\wedge} A'$, B', C', D_1', it will be shown that

$$D_1' = D'$$

To show that this is true, it is noted first that the second sequence of perspectivities, taken in reverse order, followed by the first sequence of perspectivities gives

$$A', B', C', D_1' \overline{\wedge} A, B, C, D \overline{\wedge} A', B', C', D'$$

and hence

$$A', B', C', D_1' \overline{\wedge} A', B', C', D'$$

But by Theorem 9.2 this last projectivity must leave D_1' fixed, from which it follows that D_1' is identical with D', and the theorem is proved.

Proof of the theorem for two pencils of lines is left as an exercise.

One immediate consequence of the projectivity theorem is:

Theorem 9.4

If two pencils of points on different lines are projectively related and have as a self-corresponding point, the point of intersection of the two lines, the pencils are perspectively related.

If A and A' are the self-corresponding points in two projective pencils in which also point B corresponds to point B', and point C to point C', the intersection S of the lines BB' and CC' is the center of a perspectivity which relates points A, B, C to points A', B', C'.

Proof of the following dual theorem is left as an exercise (see Exercise 2 below).

Theorem 9.5

If two pencils of lines on different points are projectively related and have as a self-corresponding line the line joining the two vertices of the pencils, the pencils are perspectively related.

EXERCISES

1. Prove Theorem 9.1 when a point A coincides with a point other than its corresponding point A'.

2. Prove Theorem 9.5.

9.5. Pappus' Theorem

An interesting application of the foregoing theory is found in a theorem credited to Pappus of Alexandria (about 340 A.D.).

About 1600 years after Pappus had proved his theorem in the Euclidean plane, Hilbert pointed out its significance in the logical development of projective geometry [2, Vol. 1, Chap. I, Sec. 3].

The importance of the theorem lies chiefly in the fact that it is frequently taken as an additional axiom of projective geometry when no use is made of points and lines outside the plane. For instance, Desargues' theorem for the plane may be proved on the basis of Axioms 1 to 6, the new assumption that, "All points are on the same plane," and Pappus' theorem, taken as an axiom.

A statement and proof of the theorem follow.

Theorem 9.6 (Pappus' Theorem)

If A, B, C are any three distinct points of a line x and A', B', C' any three distinct points of another line y, the three points of intersection

$$A'' = \begin{pmatrix} BC' \\ B'C \end{pmatrix} \qquad B'' = \begin{pmatrix} AC' \\ A'C \end{pmatrix} \qquad C'' = \begin{pmatrix} AB' \\ A'B \end{pmatrix}$$

are collinear.

PROOF. In Fig. 9.7 let

$$B_1 = \begin{pmatrix} BC' \\ AB' \end{pmatrix} \qquad C_1 = \begin{pmatrix} C'A \\ B'C \end{pmatrix}$$

Then, since the collinear points C'', B', B_1, A are perspective through point B with the respective points A', B', C', O of line y,

$$(C'', B', B_1, A) \overset{B}{\barwedge} (A', B', C', O)$$

But $\qquad (A', B', C', O) \overset{C}{\barwedge} (B'', C_1, C', A)$

and therefore

$$(C'', B', B_1, A) \barwedge (B'', C_1, C', A)$$

But, in this latter projectivity, A is a self-corresponding point, and hence, by Theorem 9.4, the projectivity is a perspectivity.   The lines

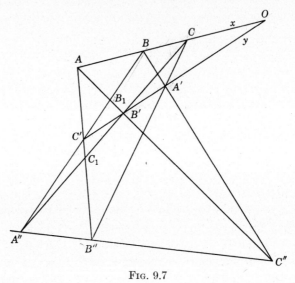

FIG. 9.7

$B''C''$, $B'C_1 (= B'C)$, and $B_1C' (= BC')$ are therefore concurrent at the point A'' of meeting of the lines $B'C$ and BC', and the theorem is proved.

PROJECTIVE THEORY OF CONICS

9.6. The New Approach to Conics

The investigations of the conics made by early Greek mathematicians were so extensive that for a long time it seemed that the last word had been said about these aesthetically appealing and extremely practical curves.

Apollonius's treatment of conics, which was one of the great mathematical achievements of antiquity, was contained in eight books, seven of which have come down to modern times.   It was a theoretical treatment, like most of those of Greek origin, and for hundreds of years the theory was unapplied.   Finally, in 1609, Kepler announced his famous law that the earth and other planets moved in elliptical orbits about the sun.   Kepler's law in turn paved the way for an even greater discovery, Newton's law of gravitation, which relies upon the fact that planetary orbits are ellipses.

Today, conics and their properties are used in many different fields. Astronomy, physics, engineering, and architecture are only a few such fields of application.

Approximately *two thousand years* after the Greeks had developed their metric theory of conics, projective nonmetric properties of these curves were discovered.   The beauty and simplicity of these latter properties have justly earned for them a place in the elementary curriculum.   It is possible that in time the new theory may lead to practical applications of even greater importance than those coming from the classical, metric theory.

There is space here for only the beginnings of this very modern and stimulating projective theory of conics.

9.7. Corresponding Elements in Two Projective Nonperspective Forms

As a preparation for introducing the projective theory of conics, a method will be explained first for locating corresponding elements in two projective nonperspective pencils of points.

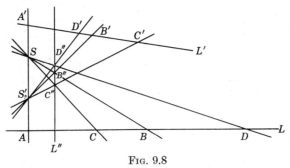

FIG. 9.8

By Theorem 9.3, not more than three points in one pencil of points and their corresponding points in the other pencil may be selected at random.   Suppose, then, that the pencil of points on line L (Fig. 9.8) is projective (*but not perspective*) with a pencil of points on a second line L', in such a way that the points A, B, C of line L correspond, respectively, to the points A', B', C' of line L'.   *It is desired to find the point D' of line L' corresponding to a fourth point D of line L.*

On any line, say AA', joining a pair of corresponding points, choose two points S and S', and join S to points of L, and S' to points of L'. In the pencils of rays at S and S', ray SS' is self-corresponding. Hence, by Theorem 9.5, these pencils are perspective, and all pairs of corresponding rays will, therefore, intersect in points of a straight line.

The intersection B'' of the corresponding rays SB, $S'B'$ and the intersection C'' of the corresponding rays SC, $S'C'$ determine the line L'' on which pairs of corresponding rays intersect.

If, then, ray SD meets L'' in a point D'', rays $S'D''$ and SD are corresponding rays, and line $S'D''$ meets line L' in the required point D'.

It is left as an exercise for the student to show that the position of D' is independent of the choice of the points S and S' on the line AA'. *Hint:* See [32, p. 67].

Dually, suppose that, in the projective pencils of lines with vertices at S and S' (Fig. 9.9), rays a, b, c of the pencil at S correspond respec-

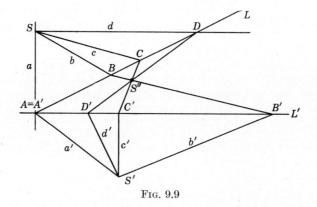

Fig. 9.9

tively to rays a', b', c' of the pencil at S', and it is desired to find the ray d' of pencil S' corresponding to a fourth ray d of the pencil at S.

Draw two lines L and L' through a point, say A, of meeting of corresponding rays, and let rays a, b, c meet L in the points A, B, C, and let rays a', b', c' meet L' in the points A, B', C', respectively. Since the two pencils of points on L and L' have point A as a self-corresponding point, these two pencils are perspective, and lines joining corresponding points pass through the point S'' of meeting of the lines BB' and CC'. If, then, ray d meets line L in point D, the line $S''D$ meets line L' in a point D' such that $S'D' = d'$ is the required ray.

It is left as an exercise for the student to show that the position of ray d' is independent of the choice of lines L and L' through the point A.

9.8. Point and Line Curves of the Second Order

Suppose now that ray d of Fig. 9.9 rotates about the point S. Then its corresponding ray d' rotates about S', and the point of intersection of corresponding rays in the two projective pencils will describe a curve C. It is proposed to study next the nature of this curve C.

In two projectively related pencils of rays, there are, at most, two pairs of corresponding rays which intersect in points of a straight line. If three pairs should intersect in collinear points, the two pencils would be perspective, and all pairs of corresponding rays would intersect on that same line. If then the pencils are not perspective, curve C is *not a straight line* but is intersected by a *straight line in, at most, two points*. For this reason, the locus of the point of intersection of corresponding rays in two projective, nonperspective pencils of lines is called *a curve of the second order*.

Dually, in two projective, nonperspective pencils of points, not more than two rays joining pairs of corresponding points can pass through any one point. As point D of Fig. 9.8 moves along the line L, its corresponding point D' moves on L', and the line DD' envelops a curve called *a line curve of the second order*.

9.9. Point and Line Conics

Curves of the second order are now called point and line conics in accordance with the dual definitions:

Point Conic

> *A point conic consists of the points of intersection of corresponding lines in two projectively related pencils of lines.*

Line Conic

> *A line conic consists of lines joining corresponding points in two projectively related pencils of points.*

The two definitions are dual if a tangent to a curve is regarded as the dual element to the point itself, and a line curve as the dual of a point curve.

It will be shown next that the curves, called conics, generated by two projective, nonperspective pencils, have properties in common with the conic given by the metric definition:

> *A conic is the locus of a point which moves so that its distance from a fixed point called the focus and from a fixed line called the directrix are in a constant ratio.*

As shown in elementary coordinate geometry (see [61, Chap. 7]), the conic may then be represented by the equation

$$ax^2 + bxy + cy^2 + dx + dy + f = 0 \qquad (1)$$

where x, y are the rectangular coordinates of any point of the curve and a, b, c, d, e, f are real constants, not all zero.

Since the equation of a line in these same coordinates is

$$gx + hy + k = 0 \qquad (2)$$

where g, h, k are real constants, $\neq$ 0, 0, 0, and since these two equations when solved simultaneously have at most two solutions, the *conic and the line meet in at most two points*. But it has already been shown (Sec. 9.8) that a line also meets the curve described by two projective, nonperspective pencils in at most two points.

Again, it will follow from either the metric or the projective definition of conics that *a conic is determined by five points*, for when coordinates of five points of the conic defined by (1) are substituted in this equation, there result five homogeneous equations in the six unknowns a, b, c, d, e, f. Except in degenerate cases, these equations have a solution for five of the unknowns in terms of the sixth, and hence *five points determine a conic*.

Conics given by the projective definitions are also determined by five points, since, it will be remembered, a projectivity is completely determined when three pairs of corresponding elements are given. If then A and B are the vertices of two projective pencils with rays AC, AD, AE corresponding, respectively, to rays BC, BD, BE, one ray of the pencil with vertex at B passes through A, and this ray meets its corresponding ray in the point A. The conic through points C, D, E, therefore, passes through A and, similarly, through point B. Thus, *the conic is determined by the three points C, D, E and the two vertices A and B*, a total of five points.

The duality principle gives similar results for line conics.

9.10. Concerning the Classification of Conics

The assignment of point and line conics of the projective plane to the various subdivisions—hyperbola, ellipse, and parabola—cannot be made at this point, because the additional concepts needed to classify conics have not as yet been introduced: distance, angle, and parallel lines are still missing. After they have been introduced, it will be possible to show that a conic defined by two projective pencils of rays is, respectively, a hyperbola, parabola, or ellipse according as two, one, or no pair of corresponding rays are parallel. Proofs of these statements are left for more advanced investigations.

In the next section, drawings of certain point and line conics will illustrate familiar curves of the elementary curriculum. The point is made in advance that only projective pencils are being used to determine points of a point conic or lines of a line conic. In other words, the curves are completely determined once the projective pencils are given.

9.11. Examples of Point and Line Conics

Some point and line conics are shown in Figs. 9.10 to 9.13.

In Fig. 9.10 the two projective pencils at S and S' are determined by the given rays a, b, c at point S and their corresponding rays a',

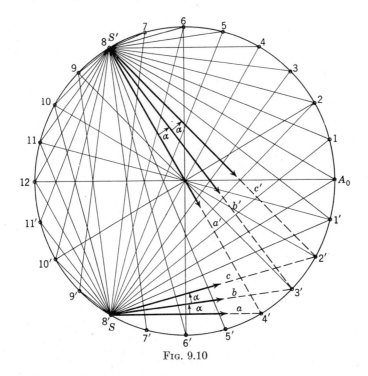

Fig. 9.10

b', c' at point S'. As ray a rotates in the clockwise direction, its corresponding ray a' rotates in the same direction. Also, the angle between any two rays, say a and b, is the same as the angle between their corresponding rays a' and b' (the pencils are then said to be congruent). In the Euclidean plane, the points of intersection of

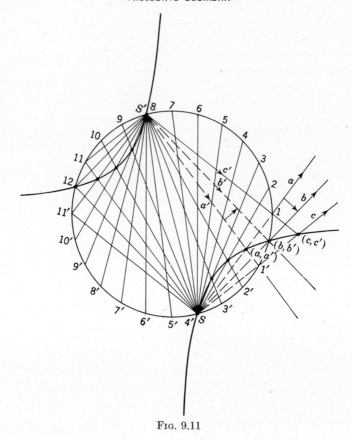

FIG. 9.11

corresponding rays lie on a circle, as shown in Sec. 4.8.   In the non-metric projective plane, the conic cannot be classified.

Figure 9.11, when viewed as a Euclidean figure, differs from Fig.

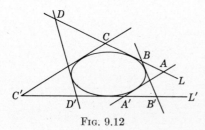

FIG. 9.12

9.10 only in the way in which angles are described.   Here, as ray a rotates in the clockwise direction, its corresponding ray a' rotates in the counterclockwise direction.   The resulting curve is a hyperbola.

Line conics are described by means of given projective pencils of points.   A line conic has already been drawn in Fig. 4.9, where lines AA', BB', CC'—joining corresponding points in the given projective pencils of points—are tangent to a circle whose center is O.

In Fig. 9.12, the lines AA', BB', CC' are tangent to an ellipse and in Fig. 9.13, to a parabola.

It will be instructive for the reader to experiment with the drawing of other point and line conics. Emphasis is being placed at this point not on the classification of these curves but on the projective pencils used in their construction.

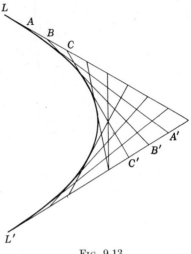

FIG. 9.13

9.12. Pascal's and Brianchon's Theorems

It is shown in Euclidean geometry that the points of intersection of the opposite sides of a hexagon inscribed in a circle are collinear [58, p. 108]. Starting with this figure, Pascal formed a cone by joining each point of the circle to a point P outside its plane. He then noted the projections of the circle and the hexagon on planes cutting the cone at various angles, and by using the fact that concurrency of lines and collinearity of points are maintained on projection, he was led to his famous theorem.

Theorem 9.7 (Pascal's Theorem)

The points of intersection of the opposite sides of a hexagon inscribed in a conic are collinear.

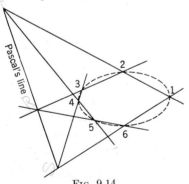

FIG. 9.14

The dual of Pascal's theorem is Brianchon's theorem.

Theorem 9.8 (Brianchon's Theorem)

The lines joining the opposite vertices of a hexagon circumscribed about a conic are concurrent.

Although Pascal discovered his theorem in the year 1640, its dual was not discovered by Brianchon until the year 1806.

Pascal's theorem is illustrated in Fig. 9.14 and Brianchon's in Fig. 9.15. The theorems, here stated without proof, are of historical rather than basic significance.

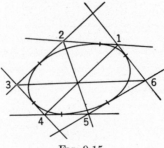

FIG. 9.15

EXERCISES

1. Show that, if, in two projectively related pencils of rays, three pairs of corresponding rays intersect in points of a straight line, the two pencils are perspective.

2. Pairs of projectively related pencils may be obtained as follows: Project all the points P on a straight line L from two different centers O and O''. In the projecting pencils, let lines a and a'', which intersect on L, correspond to each other. Prove that the two pencils are projectively related.

3. What curve of Euclidean geometry is generated by two congruent pencils of rays when angles are described in the same sense? Can you prove your answer without the aid of metric concepts? Why?

4. If Fig. 9.11 is in the Euclidean plane, how many pairs of corresponding lines are parallel in the two projective pencils generating the curve? Give reasons for your answer.

5. Is the curve of Fig. 9.13 a point or a line conic? Why?

6. Experiment with the drawing of point conics by starting with your own projective pencils of rays a, b, c at S and their corresponding rays a', b', c' at S', and show in a drawing the curve determined by points of intersection of corresponding rays in the two pencils. Can you identify your curve as an ellipse, parabola, or hyperbola?

7. Given five points of a conic and an arbitrary line through one of them, find where the line cuts the curve a second time. *Hint:* Let A, B, C, D, E (Fig. 9.16) be five given points of the required curve and let X be the arbitrary line through

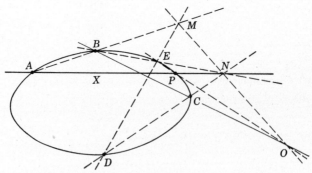

FIG. 9.16

point A. If P is the sixth point of the curve through the five points, then in the hexagon $ABCDEP$ take as pairs of opposite sides AB and DE, BC and EP, CD and PA, which is the given line X, and use Pascal's theorem to locate the point P.

SUGGESTIONS FOR FURTHER READING

(Chapters 6 to 9)

Courant, R., and H. Robbins: "What Is Mathematics?", Chap. IV.
Holgate, T. F.: "Projective Geometry."
Klein, Morris: "Mathematics in Western Cultures," Chaps. 10, 11.
Lehmer, D. N.: "An Elementary Course in Synthetic Projective Geometry."
O'Hara, C. W., and D. R. Ward: "An Introduction to Projective Geometry."
Sanger, R. G.: "Synthetic Projective Geometry."
Veblen, O., and J. W. Young: "Projective Geometry."
Winger, R. M.: "An Introduction to Projective Geometry."
Young, J. W.: "Projective Geometry."
Young, J. W. A.: "Monographs on Modern Mathematics."

Chapter 10

COORDINATE PROJECTIVE GEOMETRY

In any survey of the field of important developments in geometry, there is one subject without which no introduction to the science is complete. It is coordinate geometry, by virtue of which every geometric object and every geometric operation may be referred to the realm of numbers.

Decisive steps in the arithmetization of geometry were taken as early as 1629 by Fermat, but chief credit for this new development goes to the Frenchman Descartes, who, in 1637, published his "La Geometrie," which linked geometry with algebra and the number system and gave to the world the powerful tools needed in later developments.

Opposition to the new geometry was almost immediate, and before long, mathematicians, like politicians, were divided into rival parties, one called purists, and the other, nonpurists. The purists argued that the introduction of number concepts debased an otherwise pure science. Descartes and his followers, the nonpurists, were adamant. Figures and geometric intuition should be replaced by number concepts and algebraic theory.

The clash between the rival factions was long and bitter, but when the tumult finally quieted down, each side was found to have made concessions to the other. The purists, in their strict avoidance of the new techniques, often encountered problems in which some algebraic formulation was unavoidable. Nonpurists, on the other hand, often lost themselves in long, tiresome manipulations. It was therefore inevitable that the two viewpoints would merge.

Today, coordinate geometry and algebra take over when figures, synthetic methods, and geometric intuition fail. This fortunate turn of events is the product of a long, gradual, historical growth that has greatly enlarged the scope of classical theory.

It is assumed in what follows that the reader is already familiar with the elementary coordinate geometry of the plane and 3-space

[61], where to a point of the line there corresponds a coordinate number x, to a point of the plane a pair of coordinate numbers (x,y), and to a point of space the coordinate number triple (x,y,z), called in each case the nonhomogeneous coordinates of the point in question.

In projective geometry, it was von Staudt's algebra of throws [76, Chap. 8] which associated a real number x with each point of the line. Considerably later, the theory was extended to include the case when the coordinate x is a complex number. In current usage, *according as a coordinate geometry is based on the real or the complex number system, it is called, respectively, real or complex coordinate geometry.*

After the reader has been introduced to both systems, he will be in a better position to compare, evaluate, and appreciate the advantages of each. Certainly, a full appreciation of either geometry involves a knowledge of the other.

Attention is being directed first to *real* projective coordinate geometry.

10.1. A Euclidean Model of the Projective Plane

The study of coordinates and algebraic methods in the projective plane begins with the construction of an analytic model in which each point of the plane is represented by a triple of real numbers called *homogeneous* coordinates of the point. A Euclidean model to be used in constructing the analytic model will be described first.

In a Euclidean 3-space, consider the set of all lines through a point O of this space. Each pair of distinct lines of this set will determine a plane. The resulting set of planes, together with the totality of lines through O, constitute a model of the projective plane. To see why, first rename these lines and planes of space, calling the planes "lines" and the lines "points." Let the relation of a point being on a line be taken to mean that a line lies in a plane, as shown in the table below:

Euclidean 3-space	Projective plane
Lines through O	Points
Planes through O	Lines
Line in a plane	Point on a line

It can then be shown that *lines* and *planes* through O satisfy the axioms for *points* and *lines* of the projective plane. This is accomplished by simply recalling known properties of Euclidean 3-space.

Verification of the incidence and existence axioms is made in the parallel columns below.

Incidence Axioms

Euclidean 3-space	Projective Plane
1. If a and b are distinct lines through point O, there is at least one plane through O on both a and b.	1′. If A and B are distinct points, there is at least one line on both A and B.
2. If a and b are distinct lines through point O, there is not more than one plane through O on both a and b.	2′. If A and B are distinct points, there is not more than one line on both A and B.
3. If a plane through the origin intersects two faces of a trihedral angle whose vertex is the origin, then it intersects the third face.	3′. If a line intersects two sides of a triangle, then it intersects the third side.

Existence Axioms

4. There exists at least one plane through point O.	4′. There exists at least one line.
5. There are at least three lines on every plane through O.	5′. There are at least three distinct points on every line.
6. Not all lines through O are on the same plane through O.	6′. Not all points are on the same line.
7. Every plane through O is in Euclidean 3-space.	7′. Every line is in the plane.

Verifications of the remaining axioms and of Pappus' theorem are left as exercises.

EXERCISES

State Euclidean properties of 3-space that verify each of the following projective axioms and theorem: (a) the quadrangle axiom, (b) the separation axioms, (c) the continuity axiom, and (d) Pappus' theorem.

10.2. An Analytic Model. Homogeneous Point Coordinates

Now that points and lines of the projective plane have been represented by lines and planes of Euclidean 3-space, the analytic model may be described.

In Euclidean 3-space, let three mutually perpendicular planes x_2x_3, x_1x_3, and x_1x_2 (Fig. 10.1) intersect in a point O. Then to each point

P of this space corresponds the real number triple (x_1,x_2,x_3), where x_1, x_2, x_3 are the respective signed distances of P from these three planes.

Consider any line through the origin O of this coordinate system. Such a line is determined by a set of three direction numbers (a_1,a_2,a_3), not all of which are zero. Moreover, if t is any real number $\neq 0$, any other set (ta_1,ta_2,ta_3) determines the same line.

The number triple (a_1,a_2,a_3) is said to be equivalent to another number triple (b_1,b_2,b_3) if there exists a number $k \neq 0$ such that

$$b_1 = ka_1 \qquad b_2 = ka_2 \qquad b_3 = ka_3$$

The set of all mutually equivalent number triples forms an equivalence class which is denoted simply $\{a_1,a_2,a_3\}$. Since there exists a 1-1 correspondence between the equivalence classes $\{x_1,x_2,x_3\}$, not all of whose elements are zero, and the lines through origin of Euclidean 3-space, and since each such line is a model of a point of the projective plane, *these equivalence classes constitute an analytic model of points of the projective plane.*

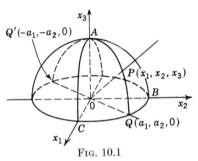

FIG. 10.1

Any representative, such as (a_1,a_2,a_3), of a particular class will be called *homogeneous coordinates of a point of the real projective plane* if the number triple is proportional to a triple of real numbers. Thus $(1,2,2)$ and $(i,2i,2i)$, where $i = \sqrt{-1}$, represent the same real point.

The picture becomes clearer if one further step is taken. Consider the hemisphere of unit radius lying above the x_1x_2 plane in Euclidean 3-space (Fig. 10.1). If a line through the origin does not lie in this plane, it cuts the hemisphere in a unique point $P(x_1,x_2,x_3)$, where

$$x_1{}^2 + x_2{}^2 + x_3{}^2 = 1$$

Furthermore, the coordinates of point P are a set of direction numbers for the line OP and hence may be used as homogeneous coordinates of the point.

One slightly disturbing feature, however, is present. A line through the origin, lying in the x_1x_2 plane, cuts the hemisphere in two points $Q(a_1,a_2,0)$ and $Q'(-a_1,-a_2,0)$. Since both of these number triples are direction numbers of the line, either one may be used as homogeneous coordinates of the point Q or Q'. To avoid having two points of the hemisphere correspond to one point of the projective plane, these two points Q_1 and Q' are now identified. With this agreement, the number triples $(a_1,a_2,0)$ and $(-a_1,-a_2,0)$ represent the same point. Points of the unit hemisphere in Euclidean 3-space then constitute another model of points of the projective plane, and Euclidean coordinates of these points may therefore be taken as homogeneous coordinates of points of the projective plane.

Remark

When the ordinary concept of distance is introduced into the projective plane and when coordinate x_3 of a point of this plane is not equal to zero, it is possible to pass from the homogeneous coordinates x_1, x_2, x_3 of the point to the nonhomogeneous coordinates x, y by the simple substitution

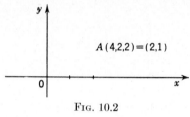

$$x = \frac{x_1}{x_3} \qquad y = \frac{x_2}{x_3}$$

Fig. 10.2

where x and y are now the respective distances of the point from two perpendicular lines OY and OX (Fig. 10.2).

In the drawings which follow, points of the projective plane for which $x_3 \neq 0$ are shown in this familiar system. Thus the point $(4,2,2)$ is represented in nonhomogeneous coordinates by the point $A(2,1)$, as shown in Fig. 10.2.

EXERCISES

1. Locate on the hemisphere of Fig. 10.1 points corresponding to each of the following points of the projective plane: $B(1,0,0)$, $C(-1,0,0)$, $D(0,1,0)$, $E(0,0,1)$, $F(1,2,3)$, $G(-1,-2,-3)$.

2. If a and b are any real numbers $\neq 0$, 0, describe the position of the point of the hemisphere corresponding to each of the following set of points: $(a,1,0)$, $(1,b,0)$, $(a,b,0)$.

3. Give the rectangular nonhomogeneous coordinates for each of the points E, F, G of Exercise 1.

4. Are there nonhomogeneous coordinates for points B, C, D of Exercise 1? Give reasons for your answer.

10.3. Lines in the Analytic Model.   Homogeneous Line Coordinates

As shown in Sec. 10.1, a projective line corresponds to a plane through the origin of Euclidean 3-space. The equation of such a plane is considered next. It is known to be

$$d_1x_1 + d_2x_2 + d_3x_3 = 0 \qquad (1)$$

where d_1, d_2, d_3 are proportional to a set of real constants $\neq 0, 0, 0$.

Since a point which satisfies (1) also satisfies the equation

$$kd_1x_1 + kd_2x_2 + kd_3x_3 = 0 \tag{2}$$

where k is any number $\neq 0$, the plane is determined either by the real number triple (d_1, d_2, d_3), not all of whose elements are zero, or by any other number triple (kd_1, kd_2, kd_3) where k is a constant $\neq 0$. A 1-1 correspondence therefore exists between the equivalence classes $\{d_1, d_2, d_3\} \neq 0, 0, 0$ and planes through the origin and hence also between these equivalence classes and lines of the projective plane.

Any representative (d_1, d_2, d_3) of the equivalence class $\{d_1, d_2, d_3\}$ will be called homogeneous line coordinates of a line of the real projective plane.

In the hemispherical model (Fig. 10.1), planes through the origin are seen to intersect the hemisphere in great semicircles whose end points are identified. These "closed semicircles" are therefore representatives of lines of the projective plane, the only exception being in the case of the x_1x_2 plane, which cuts the hemisphere in a circle. But, because we have agreed (in Sec. 10.2) to identify diametrically opposite points on this boundary circle, the latter also represents a projective line, i.e., the one with homogeneous line coordinates $(0,0,1)$.

Other examples of line coordinates are $(1,0,0)$ and $(0,1,0)$, corresponding to the respective semicircles AC and AB of Fig. 10.1.

10.4. Incidence of Points and Lines

In the axiomatic definition of a projective plane, the concept of incidence of point and line was undefined. It was, however, required to satisfy certain conditions called incidence axioms. This same concept of incidence, in the case of the analytic model, takes a concrete form now to be explained.

The incidence of a point and a line follows from the fact that the corresponding line through the origin lies in the appropriate plane through the origin. Since the equation of such a plane is

$$d_1x_1 + d_2x_2 + d_3x_3 = 0 \tag{1}$$

and the parametric equations of such a line are

$$x_1 = a_1t \qquad x_2 = a_2t \qquad x_3 = a_3t \tag{2}$$

where a_1, a_2, a_3 are its direction cosines, the line will lie in the plane if its coordinates satisfy the equation of the plane for all t; i.e., if

$$d_1a_1 + d_2a_2 + d_3a_3 = 0 \tag{3}$$

Since the converse statement also holds, proof has been given of the following theorem:

Theorem 10.1

A point with homogeneous coordinates (a_1, a_2, a_3) and a line with homogeneous coordinates (d_1, d_2, d_3) are incident if and only if

$$d_1 a_1 + d_2 a_2 + d_3 a_3 = 0$$

When the point has homogeneous coordinates (x_1, x_2, x_3), (3) takes the standard form

$$d_1 x_1 + d_2 x_2 + d_3 x_3 = 0 \qquad (4)$$

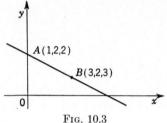

Fig. 10.3

called the *point equation of the line.* Equation (4) is therefore the analytic representation of a pencil of points.

To obtain the point equation of the line through the two given points $A(1,2,2)$ and $B(3,2,3)$, as shown in Fig. 10.3, it is noted first that point A will lie on the line (4) if and only if

$$d_1 + 2d_2 + 2d_3 = 0$$

and point B lies on the line if and only if

$$3d_1 + 2d_2 + 3d_3 = 0$$

From the theory of equations it is then known that d_1, d_2, and d_3 satisfy the relation

$$d_1 : d_2 : d_3 = \begin{vmatrix} 2 & 2 \\ 2 & 3 \end{vmatrix} : - \begin{vmatrix} 1 & 2 \\ 3 & 3 \end{vmatrix} : \begin{vmatrix} 1 & 2 \\ 3 & 2 \end{vmatrix}$$

and hence the point equation of line AB is

$$2x_1 + 3x_2 - 4x_3 = 0$$

Now consider Eq. (4) from another point of view. This time suppose that the point (x_1, x_2, x_3) is fixed and the coefficients d_1, d_2, d_3 vary. Then, to each number triple (d_1, d_2, d_3) satisfying (4) there corresponds a line L through the fixed point (x_1, x_2, x_3). Equation (4) therefore represents a pencil of lines through this point.

It is well now to distinguish between number triples which represent points and those which represent lines. This will be done by using the number triple (x_1, x_2, x_3) to represent a variable point and the number triple (u_1, u_2, u_3) to represent a variable line.

The linear equation

$$a_1 u_1 + a_2 u_2 + a_3 u_3 = 0$$

is the *line equation of the fixed point* (a_1, a_2, a_3) in accordance with the definition:

A line equation of a point is an equation in variable line coordinates (u_1, u_2, u_3) which is satisfied by the coordinates of only those lines which pass through the point.

The line equation of the point $(2, 3, -4)$ of Fig. 10.4 is

$$2u_1 + 3u_2 - 4u_3 = 0$$

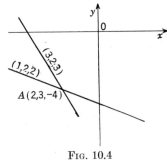

and line coordinates of two lines of this pencil are $(1,2,2)$ and $(3,2,3)$. Proofs of these statements are left as exercises.

Since the equation:

$$u_1 x_1 + u_2 x_2 + u_3 x_3 = 0$$

Fig. 10.4

represents a point, if the x's are fixed and the u's are variables, or a line, if the u's are fixed and the x's are variables, the statement

$$2 \cdot 3 + 3 \cdot 2 - 4 \cdot 3 = 0$$

may be taken to mean that the point $(3,2,3)$ lies on the line $(2,3,-4)$ or that the point $(2,3,-4)$ lies on the line $(3,2,3)$. This symmetry is the basis of duality between point and line in analytic (coordinate) projective geometry.

10.5. Coordinates in the General Projective Plane

It has been shown in the preceding sections that certain models are actually representations of a projective plane, but it has not yet been shown that any projective plane can be so represented. Nevertheless, such a representation is always possible. To prove this statement, it is necessary to introduce coordinates into the projective plane in a systematic way, using only the given axioms. These coordinates must then be shown to have all the desired properties of elements of the projective plane. Because this process is extremely lengthy, tedious, and somewhat tiresome, details are omitted here, and the interested reader is referred to the literature [46, Chaps. 7, 8]. The net result is to show that the models which have been given here are in no way special and actually do represent the geometry of the projective plane.

EXERCISES

1. Locate on the hemisphere of Fig. 10.1 semicircles corresponding to each of the lines whose point equations are

$$x_1 + x_2 + x_3 = 0$$
$$x_3 = 0$$

2. Show in a drawing the points represented by each of the following line equations:

$$u_1 + u_2 + u_3 = 0$$
$$u_3 = 0$$

3. Locate the point represented by the line equation

$$u_1 - u_2 = 0$$

4. Give a set of line coordinates for two different lines through the point defined in Exercise 3. Show the point and the lines in a drawing.

5. Plot and find homogeneous coordinates for the point of intersection of each of the following pairs of lines:

(a) $2x_1 - 3x_2 + 4x_3 = 0$
    $4x_1 + 6x_2 + \ \ x_3 = 0$
(b) $2x_1 - 3x_2 + 4x_3 = 0$
    $4x_1 - 6x_2 + \ \ x_3 = 0$

6. (a) What locus is represented by the following pair of line equations:

$$2u_1 - 3u_2 + 4u_3 = 0$$
$$4u_1 - 6u_2 + \ \ u_3 = 0$$

(b) Show the locus in a drawing.

7. Show that the points (lines) (a_1, a_2, a_3) and (b_1, b_2, b_3) are not distinct if there exist constants $k, l \neq 0, 0$ such that

$$ka_i + lb_i = 0 \qquad i = 1, 2, 3$$

10.6. Analytic Expressions for Collinearity of Points and Concurrency of Lines

Consider now the following equation in determinant form:

$$\begin{vmatrix} x_1 & x_2 & x_3 \\ a_1 & a_2 & a_3 \\ b_1 & b_2 & b_3 \end{vmatrix} = 0 \qquad\qquad (1)$$

Since this equation is linear in the point coordinates x_1, x_2, x_3, it is the equation of a line; and since the equation is satisfied by the points $A(a_1, a_2, a_3)$ and $B(b_1, b_2, b_3)$, it is the equation of the line through these two points.

Only algebraic theory (see Exercise 5 below) is needed to show that a third point $C(c_1, c_2, c_3)$ will lie on line (1) if and only if

$$\begin{vmatrix} a_1 & a_2 & a_3 \\ b_1 & b_2 & b_3 \\ c_1 & c_2 & c_3 \end{vmatrix} = 0 \qquad (2)$$

Hence (2) is a necessary and sufficient condition for collinearity of the three points (a_1,a_2,a_3), (b_1,b_2,b_3), and (c_1,c_2,c_3).

Dually, the following equation in line coordinates:

$$\begin{vmatrix} u_1 & u_2 & u_3 \\ \alpha_1 & \alpha_2 & \alpha_3 \\ \beta_1 & \beta_2 & \beta_3 \end{vmatrix} = 0 \qquad (3)$$

is the line equation of a point, and two lines through the point are $(\alpha_1,\alpha_2,\alpha_3)$ and $(\beta_1,\beta_2,\beta_3)$. A third line $(\gamma_1,\gamma_2,\gamma_3)$ will pass through the point if and only if

$$\begin{vmatrix} \alpha_1 & \alpha_2 & \alpha_3 \\ \beta_1 & \beta_2 & \beta_3 \\ \gamma_1 & \gamma_2 & \gamma_3 \end{vmatrix} = 0 \qquad (4)$$

Thus (4) is the necessary and sufficient condition for concurrency of the lines $(\alpha_1,\alpha_2,\alpha_3)$, $(\beta_1,\beta_2,\beta_3)$, and $(\gamma_1,\gamma_2,\gamma_3)$ (see Exercise 6 below).

EXERCISES

1. Show that the points $(0,2,3)$, $(3,0,3)$, $(2,2,4)$ are not collinear.

2. Plot the lines represented by the number triples of Exercise 1. Are they concurrent? Why?

3. For what value of k are the lines $x_1 - x_2 - x_3 = 0$, $2x_1 + x_2 + kx_3 = 0$, $7x_1 - x_2 + 3x_3 = 0$ concurrent?

4. (a) Plot the triangle with its vertices at the points $A(2,2,1)$, $B(2,0,1)$, $C(3,1,1)$ and the triangle having vertices $A'(4,4,1)$, $B'(6,0,1)$, $C'(12,4,3)$.

(b) Find coordinates of the points of meeting of the pairs of lines AB, $A'B'$; AC, $A'C'$; BC, $B'C'$; and show that these points are collinear.

(c) Find line coordinates for the lines AA', BB', CC', and show that these lines are concurrent.

(d) What famous theorem is illustrated in your drawing?

5. (a) Show that a necessary condition that the three points (a_1,a_2,a_3), (b_1,b_2,b_3), and (c_1,c_2,c_3) lie on a line is that Eq. (3) of the preceding section be satisfied. (b) Is this condition sufficient to ensure the collinearity of points? Prove your answer. *Hint:* See [16, Chap. 13].

6. Dualize the theory of Exercise 5.

10.7. Coordinates of Points of a Pencil; Lines of a Pencil

A method will be explained now for determining a pair of numbers representing a set of homogeneous coordinates for a point of a pencil of points or a line of a pencil of lines. The method and its dual are contained in the proofs of the dual theorems:

Theorem 10.2

If $A(a_1,a_2,a_3)$ and $B(b_1,b_2,b_3)$ are any two distinct points of a pencil of points, any point P of the pencil has the homogeneous coordinates $(\lambda_2 a_1 + \lambda_1 b_1,\ \lambda_2 a_2 + \lambda_1 b_2,\ \lambda_2 a_3 + \lambda_1 b_3)$, where λ_1 and λ_2 are real constants $\neq 0, 0$.

Theorem 10.3

If $a(a_1,a_2,a_3)$ and $b(b_1,b_2,b_3)$ are any two distinct lines of a pencil of lines, any line p of the pencil has the homogeneous coordinates $(\lambda_2 a_1 + \lambda_1 b_1,\ \lambda_2 a_2 + \lambda_1 b_2,\ \lambda_2 a_3 + \lambda_1 b_3)$, where λ_1 and λ_2 are real constants $\neq 0, 0$.

The proof of Theorem 10.2 follows from the fact that the coordinates of any point $P(x_1,x_2,x_3)$ on the line through the given points $A(a_1,a_2,a_3)$ and $B(b_1,b_2,b_3)$ must satisfy Eq. (1), Sec. 10.6. From the theory of algebra [16, Chap. 13], it then follows that there exist constants k, l, $m \neq 0, 0, 0$ such that

$$mx_i = ka_i + lb_i \qquad i = 1,\ 2,\ 3 \qquad (1)$$

Now, $m \neq 0$; for, if $m = 0$, $ka_i + lb_i = 0$, and the points A and B would not be distinct. Hence, if

$$\lambda_1 = \frac{l}{m} \qquad \lambda_2 = \frac{k}{m}$$

then

$$x_i = \lambda_2 a_i + \lambda_1 b_i \qquad i = 1,\ 2,\ 3 \qquad (2)$$

and the theorem is proved.

The pair of numbers λ_1, $\lambda_2 \neq 0, 0$ are homogeneous coordinates of a point on the line through the fixed points $A(a_1,a_2,a_3)$ and $B(b_1,b_2,b_3)$.

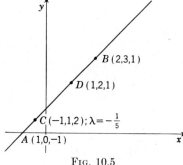

FIG. 10.5

If $\lambda_2 \neq 0$, then to each point of the line corresponds a single parameter value λ, where $\lambda = \lambda_1/\lambda_2$. To the value $\lambda = 0$ corresponds the fixed point A. (Why?)

If $\lambda_2 = 0$, it is agreed that $\lambda = \infty$ corresponds to the fixed point B of the line.

A particular example will illustrate the method. Suppose a parameter value is desired for the point $C(-1,1,2)$ of the line through $A(1,0,-1)$ and $B(2,3,1)$ (Fig. 10.5). Then from (1)

$$k + 2l + m = 0$$
$$3l - m = 0$$
$$-k + l - 2m = 0$$

and hence

$$k:l:m = -5:1:3$$

Therefore:

$$\lambda_1 = \frac{l}{m} = \frac{1}{3}$$

$$\lambda_2 = \frac{k}{m} = -\frac{5}{3}$$

and

$$\lambda = \frac{\lambda_1}{\lambda_2} = -\frac{1}{5}$$

Thus to the point $C(-1,1,2)$ corresponds the number pair $(-1,5)$, or any number pair of the set $(-r,5r)$ with $r \neq 0$, and C has the single parameter $\lambda = -\frac{1}{5}$. This latter coordinate does not represent, as in elementary coordinate geometry, the distance of the point C from a fixed point, but rather a coordinate with reference to the two fixed points A and B called *base points*.

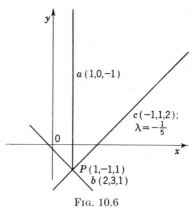

Proof of the dual Theorem 10.3 is left as an exercise (see Exercise 3 below), and dual results are illustrated in Fig. 10.6, where the base

Fig. 10.6

lines $a(1,0,-1)$ and $b(2,3,1)$ intersect at the point $P(1,-1,1)$, and line $c(-1,1,2)$ has for its parameter value $\lambda = -\frac{1}{5}$.

EXERCISES

1. Find nonhomogeneous coordinates of each of the four points A, B, C, D of Fig. 10.5, when A and B are the base points and when C and D are the base points.

2. Find a parameter value for the line $(2,-1,-3)$ through the point of meeting of the lines $(1,0,-1)$ and $(2,3,1)$.

3. Prove Theorem 10.3.

10.8 Cross-ratio Formulas

When four elements P_i, $i = 1, \ldots, 4$, of a one-dimensional form have homogeneous coordinates (x_i, t_i) with reference to two base elements, the cross ratio (P_1P_2, P_3P_4) of these elements is, by definition, the quantity

$$(P_1P_2, P_3P_4) = \frac{\begin{vmatrix} x_3 & t_3 \\ x_1 & t_1 \end{vmatrix} \begin{vmatrix} x_2 & t_2 \\ x_4 & t_4 \end{vmatrix}}{\begin{vmatrix} x_2 & t_2 \\ x_3 & t_3 \end{vmatrix} \begin{vmatrix} x_4 & t_4 \\ x_1 & t_1 \end{vmatrix}} \tag{1}$$

If λ_i is the nonhomogeneous coordinate or parameter of the element P_i, (1) reduces to the formula

$$(P_1P_2,P_3P_4) = \frac{(\lambda_3 - \lambda_1)(\lambda_2 - \lambda_4)}{(\lambda_2 - \lambda_3)(\lambda_4 - \lambda_1)} \tag{2}$$

which may be used when no parameter is infinite.

As in the earlier definition of cross ratio (Sec. 4.5), the ordering of the elements is significant. There is a cross ratio corresponding to each of the 24 permutations of the four letters P_1, P_2, P_3, P_4, and these 24 cross ratios fall into six sets of four each in accordance with Theorems 4.10 to 4.12. Proofs, which are left as exercises, depend only on algebraic manipulation of formula (1) or (2).

In a geometry in which distance has been defined and the coordinates of the points P_i, $i = 1, \ldots, 4$, are the respective distances x_1, x_2, x_3, x_4 from a fixed point of the line, Eq. (2) reduces to the formula

$$(P_1P_2,P_3P_4) = \frac{(x_3 - x_1)(x_2 - x_4)}{(x_2 - x_3)(x_4 - x_1)} = \frac{(P_1P_3/P_3P_2)}{P_1P_4/P_4P_2}$$

The last fraction in this formula is, as in Sec. 4.5, the quotient of the ratios into which points P_3 and P_4 divide the line segment P_1P_2. This result is unexpected in view of the fact that distance has not yet been defined in the present development.

EXERCISES

1. If E_1, E_2, E_3, E_4 are distinct elements of a pencil of points (pencil of lines) whose homogeneous coordinates are, respectively,

$$(a_i) \qquad (b_i) \qquad (a_i + \lambda_1 b_i) \qquad (a_i + \lambda_2 b_i) \qquad i = 1, \ldots, 3$$

show that $(E_1E_2,E_3E_4) = \lambda_1/\lambda_2$.

2. If A, B, C are any three points on the line through two given points O and U, show that the cross ratios (OU,AB), (OU,BC), and (OU,AC) satisfy the relation:

$$(OU,AB) \cdot (OU,BC) = (OU,AC)$$

10.9. Cross Ratios When Elements Are Not Distinct

Limit processes are used to define the cross ratio of four elements when two of them coincide. Thus, by definition

$$(P_1P_2,P_3P_3) = \lim_{P_4 \to P_3} (P_1P_2,P_3P_4) = 1$$
$$(P_1P_2,P_3P_2) = \lim_{P_4 \to P_2} (P_1P_2,P_3P_4) = 0$$
$$(P_1P_2,P_3P_1) = \lim_{P_4 \to P_1} (P_1P_2,P_3P_4) = \infty$$

Definitions covering the remaining cross ratios in which two of the elements are the same may be obtained by using Theorems 4.10 to 4.12, which are valid when two of the elements coincide. For example, from the formula

$$(P_1P_2,P_3P_4) = (P_3P_4,P_1P_2)$$

follows the formula

$$(P_3P_3,P_1P_2) = 1$$

10.10. Complex Geometry

So far in the present development of coordinate geometry, only triples of real numbers or numbers proportional to them have been used in representing points and lines. A brief introduction will be given now to *complex geometry*, in which points and lines are represented by triples of *complex* numbers.

A complex number, it will be recalled, is a number of the form

$$a + bi$$

where a and b are real numbers and $i = \sqrt{-1}$. If $b = 0$, the complex number is real, and if $b \neq 0$, the number is said to be "nonreal." Real numbers are therefore embedded in the complex system, and this fact has been used to extend and generalize algebraic theory. For example, the equation

$$x^2 + 1 = 0$$

which has no solution in the real-number field, has the two solutions $\pm i$ in the complex-number field, in accordance with the theorem:

Theorem 10.4

Any algebraic equation with complex coefficients may be solved in terms of complex numbers, and the number of solutions is equal to the degree of the equation.

The simplicity of expression introduced into algebra by extending the real number system has its counterpart in geometry. A simple example will illustrate.

In elementary coordinate geometry, where nonhomogeneous coordinates x, y of a point of the plane are real numbers, the unit circle and the line (Fig. 10.7) are represented by the respective equations:

$$x^2 + y^2 = 1$$
$$x = b \tag{1}$$

If b is a real number whose absolute value is less than unity, the two loci meet at the points

$$P(b, \sqrt{1 - b^2}) \qquad Q(b, -\sqrt{1 - b^2})$$

whose coordinates are solutions of (1).

If, however, $b > 1$, system (1) has the solutions

$$x = b \qquad y = \pm \sqrt{1 - b^2} \qquad b > 1$$

whose y values are complex. Consequently, there is no point of the real plane corresponding to either one of the number pair $(b, \sqrt{1 - b^2})$ and $(b, -\sqrt{1 - b^2})$. In this case, the conic and the line fail to meet (Fig. 10.8). However, the aim of modern geometers is to set up a systematic geometry in which a conic and a line always meet and have

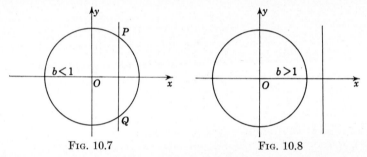

FIG. 10.7   FIG. 10.8

as coordinates a common solution of the equations representing their loci.

There are two ways to accomplish this aim. The real plane may be extended to include points whose homogeneous coordinates are proportional to complex numbers, and existing theory modified accordingly; or, a geometry of the complex plane may be developed without any reference to the real plane [46, Chap. 7; 67, Vol. II].

The less formal plan of introducing complex geometry as an extension and modification of the real system is contemplated and will suffice here, since complex points and lines will be used only to clarify and extend certain theory of the real plane. (No advanced theory of the complex plane is needed for this purpose.) By viewing real geometry as part of the complex system, limitations and exceptions occurring in the real plane are seen in their proper perspective.

10.11. Complex Points

As already shown, the *real* projective plane consists of all equivalent triples of real homogeneous coordinates except (0,0,0). To extend this system, consider the set of all equivalent triples of complex homogeneous coordinates (x_1, x_2, x_3). It is agreed that an equivalence triple

$\{x_1, x_2, x_3\}$ represents the set of numbers

$$(\rho x_1, \rho x_2, \rho x_3)$$

where ρ is any complex number $\neq 0$. *Each equivalence triple $\{x_1, x_2, x_3\}$ is called a complex point, and the totality of these points constitutes the complex plane.*

The complex point $\{x_1, x_2, x_3\}$ is said to be *real* if it has one set of real homogeneous coordinates; otherwise, it is *nonreal*. For example,

$$(2 - 2i,\ 0,\ 4 - 4i) \qquad (2i, 0, 4i) \qquad (2, 0, 4)$$

all represent the same real point A. On the other hand, all the number triples

$$(2, 0, 4i) \qquad (6i, 0, -12) \qquad (1, 0, 2i)$$

represent the same nonreal point B. Both points A and B are complex.

10.12. Complex Lines

In Sec. 10.4, line L of the real plane was represented analytically by the linear equation

$$u_1 x_1 + u_2 x_2 + u_3 x_3 = 0 \tag{1}$$

in x_1, x_2, x_3, where the number triple (x_1, x_2, x_3) represents a variable point of the line and u_1, u_2, u_3 are constants. Both number triples were assumed to be proportional to a set of real numbers $\neq 0, 0, 0$.

This representation of the line is now extended to the complex plane by the assumption that each of the number triples is proportional to a triple of complex numbers $\neq 0, 0, 0$. It is then agreed that (1) is the condition that the complex point (x_1, x_2, x_3) lie on the complex line whose line coordinates are u_1, u_2, u_3.

If one set of line coordinates for L is proportional to a set of real numbers, the complex line is *real;* otherwise, it is *nonreal*. For example,

$$2i x_1 + 0 x_2 + 4i x_3 = 0 \tag{2}$$

is a real line with line coordinates $\{2, 0, 4\}$, and

$$2 x_1 + 0 x_2 + 4i x_3 = 0 \tag{3}$$

is a nonreal line with line coordinates $\{2, 0, 4i\}$.

If, on the other hand, the point (x_1, x_2, x_3) is fixed and (u_1, u_2, u_3) is a variable number triple, then (1) represents a family of complex lines through the fixed point. It is called the line equation of the point, (x_1, x_2, x_3). For example,

$$2i u_1 + 0 u_2 + 4i u_3 = 0 \tag{4}$$

is the line equation of the *real* point $(2,0,4) = (2i,0,4i)$, and

$$2u_1 + 0u_2 + 4iu_3 = 0$$

is the line equation of the *nonreal* point $(2,0,4i)$.

Other examples of point and line equations are

$$x_3 = 0$$

which is the real line whose line coordinates are $(0,0,1)$, and

$$u_1 + iu_2 = 0$$

which is the nonreal point with coordinates $(1,i,0)$.

10.13. The Two-dimensional Character of the Complex Line

Because the algebra of complex numbers is the same as that of real numbers, much of the theory of the real plane carries over immediately to the complex plane.   For instance, Eq. (1), Sec. 10.6, is the point equation of the line through the complex points $A(a_1,a_2,a_3)$ and $B(b_1,b_2,b_3)$, and Eq. (2) of this same section is the line equation of the point of meeting of the complex lines a and b.

Since two complex points determine a line and two complex lines determine a point, incidence axioms for real points and lines hold when these elements are complex.   The same is true of the existence axioms (see Exercise 3 below), but in attempting to extend the theory of Sec. 10.6 to the complex plane, a first basic difference is noted between the two systems.   In the real plane, the line is a one-dimensional continuum.   In the complex plane, the line is a two-dimensional continuum, and separation axioms no longer hold.   This is seen most easily by recalling the arguments of Sec. 10.6.

With each point P of the real line there is associated a pair of real numbers $(\lambda_1,\lambda_2) \neq 0, 0$.   Provided that $\lambda_2 \neq 0$, a nonhomogeneous coordinate $\lambda = \lambda_1/\lambda_2$ is assigned to each point of the line, and when $\lambda_2 = 0$, λ is arbitrarily put equal to ∞.   The point $P(\infty)$ is called the point at infinity on the line, or the ideal point of the line.   The projective line then appears as an ordinary (Euclidean) line with a single point at infinity appearing at both "ends."

When the underlying number system changes from the real to the complex system, all numbers in these arguments are taken to be complex, and $P(\lambda)$ is then a point of the complex line.

If now the complex coordinate λ of point P is written

$$\lambda = x + iy$$

then to each value of λ and hence to each point $P(\lambda)$ of the complex line corresponds the number pair (x,y). The complex line then becomes a two-dimensional entity which can be brought into 1-1 correspondence with the Gauss (complex) plane, in which each point is represented by the nonhomogeneous coordinates (x,y). Points on the x axis of this Gauss plane correspond to complex points with real coordinates.

Since complex numbers cannot be ordered, separation axioms of the real plane must be denied in the complex plane, and in their place is a theory of chains. It is at this point that real and complex geometries take separate paths.

EXERCISES

1. Find the equation of the line determined by the points $(1,\ i,\ 3 + 2i)$ and $(1,\ -i,\ 3 - 2i)$.

2. If the number triples of Exercise 1 denote lines, find coordinates of the point of meeting of these lines.

3. Show that complex points and lines satisfy existence axioms for real points and lines.

10.14. Conjugate Complex Elements

The complex numbers

$$x = a + bi \qquad \bar{x} = a - bi$$

are *conjugates*. Like numbers, complex points and lines may also be conjugates in accordance with the definition:

Two elements are conjugate complex if, when (a_1, a_2, a_3) are homogeneous coordinates of one, $(\bar{a}_1, \bar{a}_2, \bar{a}_3)$ are homogeneous coordinates of the other.

For example $(1,\ i,\ 3 + 2i)$ and $(1,\ -i,\ 3 - 2i)$ are conjugate elements, and in this case corresponding coordinates are conjugates. However, because homogeneous coordinates admit a proportionality factor, homogeneous coordinates of two conjugate complex elements need not be the number triples (a_1, a_2, a_3) and $(\bar{a}_1, \bar{a}_2, \bar{a}_3)$. For example, the number triples

$$(2,\ i,\ 1 - i) \qquad \text{and} \qquad (2 + 2i,\ 1 - i,\ 2i)$$

represent conjugate complex elements, and yet corresponding numbers are not conjugates. An alternative number triple representing this second element is

$$(2,\ -i,\ 1 + i)$$

In the proofs of the following theorems, use is made of the fact that, when two conjugate numbers $a + bi$ and $a - bi$ are equal, $b = 0$ and the numbers are real.

Theorem 10.5

If a point $P(x_1,x_2,x_3)$ lies on a line $L(u_1,u_2,u_3)$, the conjugate complex point $\bar{P}(\bar{x}_1,\bar{x}_2,\bar{x}_3)$ lies on the conjugate complex line $\bar{L}(\bar{u}_1,\bar{u}_2,\bar{u}_3)$.

PROOF. The conjugate of the complex number $u_1x_1 + u_2x_2 + u_3x_3$ is the complex number $\bar{u}_1\bar{x}_1 + \bar{u}_2\bar{x}_2 + \bar{u}_3\bar{x}_3$ (see Exercise 1 below). Also, if a complex number $a + bi$ is zero, $a = b = 0$, and its conjugate $a - bi$ is also zero. Therefore if

$$u_1x_1 + u_2x_2 + u_3x_3 = 0$$

then
$$\bar{u}_1\bar{x}_1 + \bar{u}_2\bar{x}_2 + \bar{u}_3\bar{x}_3 = 0$$

But this last equation is the condition that the point $\bar{P}(\bar{x}_1,\bar{x}_2,\bar{x}_3)$ lie on the line $\bar{L}(\bar{u}_1,\bar{u}_2,\bar{u}_3)$, and thus the theorem is proved.

Theorem 10.6

There is one and only one real point on a nonreal complex line.

PROOF. The nonreal complex line L, whose equation is

$$u_1x_1 + u_2x_2 + u_3x_3 = 0$$

may be expressed in the form

$$(u'_1 + iu''_1)x_1 + (u'_2 + iu''_2)x_2 + (u'_3 + iu''_3)x_3 = 0$$

where u'_i and u''_i, $i = 1, 2, 3$, are all real numbers and at least one of the u''_i is not equal to zero.

A real number triple (y_1,y_2,y_3) representing a real point will therefore satisfy this equation if

$$u'_1y_1 + u'_2y_2 + u'_3y_3 = 0$$
and
$$u''_1y_1 + u''_2y_2 + u''_3y_3 = 0$$

It is known from the theory of algebra that these equations have the solution

$$y_1 = k \begin{vmatrix} u'_2 & u'_3 \\ u''_2 & u''_3 \end{vmatrix} \qquad y_2 = k \begin{vmatrix} u'_3 & u'_1 \\ u''_3 & u''_1 \end{vmatrix} \qquad y_3 = k \begin{vmatrix} u'_1 & u'_2 \\ u''_1 & u''_2 \end{vmatrix}$$

where k is a constant $\neq 0$. Hence the nonreal line L contains the real point (y_1,y_2,y_3).

If there were a second real point on L, the line would be real, contrary to hypothesis. Thus the theorem is proved.

The dual theorem whose proof is left as an exercise is:

Theorem 10.7

There is one and only one real line on a nonreal point.

EXERCISES

1. Show that the complex numbers $u_1x_1 + u_2x_2 + u_3x_3$ and $\bar{u}_1\bar{x}_1 + \bar{u}_2\bar{x}_2 + \bar{u}_3\bar{x}_3$ are conjugates.

2. Prove the following theorems:

(a) The point of intersection of two conjugate complex lines is a real point.

(b) The line determined by two conjugate complex points is a real line.

3. Find the real point on the nonreal line $(2, i, 3 - 4i)$. [*Hint:* Let (y_1, y_2, y_3) be the real point. Then $2y_1 + 3y_3 = 0$ and $y_2 - 4y_3 = 0$.]

4. Show that the line which joins the nonreal points $(1, i, 3 - 2i)$ and $(1, -i, 3 + 2i)$ is a real line.

5. Find the real point on the nonreal line $(2, i, 3 - 4i)$ and the real line through the nonreal point $(1, i, 0)$.

10.15. Conics

It is now possible to sketch briefly the method by which the equation of a point conic of the real plane is obtained from the projective definition (Sec. 9.9), in which a point conic is defined as the locus of points of intersection of corresponding lines in two projectively related pencils of lines.

Let a conic be generated by two projective pencils in which the base lines m and n of one pencil correspond to the respective base lines p and q of the other; and let equations of these lines be:

$$
\begin{aligned}
m: & \quad m_1x_1 + m_2x_2 + m_3x_3 = 0 \\
n: & \quad n_1x_1 + n_2x_2 + n_3x_3 = 0
\end{aligned}
\tag{1}
$$

$$
\begin{aligned}
p: & \quad p_1x_1 + p_2x_2 + p_3x_3 = 0 \\
q: & \quad q_1x_1 + q_2x_2 + q_3x_3 = 0
\end{aligned}
\tag{2}
$$

The two pencils are then represented by the equations

$$ m + \lambda n = 0 \quad\quad \text{and} \quad\quad p + \mu q = 0 \tag{3} $$

where λ and μ are corresponding values of the parameters in the two pencils. Use is made now of the following theorem:*

---

* For proof of this theorem, see [76, p. 47].

Theorem 10.8

Any projective correspondence between the elements of two one-dimensional forms may be represented by the relation

$$\mu = \frac{a\lambda + b}{c\lambda + d} \tag{4}$$

between the parameters of the two forms, where a, b, c, d are real numbers subject to the condition

$$\begin{vmatrix} a & b \\ c & d \end{vmatrix} \neq 0$$

For special choices of the basic elements, (4) reduces to

$$\mu = k\lambda \tag{5}$$

To obtain the equation of a conic in this case, it is therefore only necessary to eliminate λ and μ from (3) and (5). There results the equation

$$np - kmq = 0$$

which through the use of (1) and (2) becomes the second-degree equation in x_1, x_2, x_3:

$$A x_1{}^2 + B x_1 x_2 + C x_2{}^2 + D x_1 x_3 + E x_2 x_3 + F x_3{}^2 = 0 \tag{6}$$

whose coefficients are real numbers.

Of interest later are the special conic:

$$x_1{}^2 + x_2{}^2 - x_3{}^2 = 0$$

and the degenerate conic:

$$x_3{}^2 = 0$$

Dually, the second-degree equation in line coordinates u_1, u_2, u_3:

$$a u_1{}^2 + b u_1 u_2 + c u_2{}^2 + d u_1 u_3 + e u_2 u_3 + f u_3{}^2 = 0$$

with real coefficients, represents a line conic. Special line conics for later use are:

$$u_1{}^2 + u_2{}^2 + k u_3{}^2 = 0$$

where k is a constant, $\neq 0$, and

$$u_1{}^2 + u_2{}^2 = 0$$

10.16. Real and Nonreal Conics

Attention was confined in the preceding discussion to conics in the real projective plane. For the extension of the theory to the complex plane in which the real plane is embedded, the reader is referred to the literature [67, Chap. 5]. All that will be needed of this theory in what follows are the definitions:

A real conic is one whose equation has real coefficients and which contains at least one real point. If the conic contains no real point, it is said to be a nonreal conic.

For example, the point conic

$$x_1{}^2 + x_2{}^2 + kx_3{}^2 = 0$$

is *real* if $k = -1$, *nonreal* if $k = 1$, and *degenerate* if $k = 0$. Since

$$x_1{}^2 + x_2{}^2 = (x_1 + ix_2)(x_1 - ix_2) = 0$$

the degenerate conic consists of the two lines:

$$x_1 + ix_2 = 0$$
$$x_1 - ix_2 = 0$$

which intersect in the real point $(0,0,1)$ (see Exercise 1 below).

Dually, the line conic

$$u_1{}^2 + u_2{}^2 + ku_3{}^2 = 0$$

is *real* if $k = -1$, *nonreal* if $k = 1$, and *degenerate* if $k = 0$. Since

$$u_1{}^2 + u_2{}^2 = (u_1 + iu_2)(u_1 - iu_2) = 0$$

the degenerate line conic represents the two special conjugate points:

$$I(1,i,0) \qquad J(1,-i,0)$$

called, for reasons to be explained later, the *circular points at infinity* (see Sec. 11.11). Proof that the line joining these points is the real line $x_3 = 0$ is left as an exercise (see Exercise 2 below).

EXERCISES

1. Show that the lines $x_1 + ix_2 = 0$ and $x_1 - ix_2 = 0$ intersect in the real point $(0,0,1)$.

2. Show that the line joining the circular points at infinity, $I(1,i,0)$ and $J(1,-i,0)$, is the real line $x_3 = 0$.

Concluding Remarks

In this chapter, points of the real projective plane were represented by number triples (x_1,x_2,x_3) proportional to real numbers, and lines by linear equations in these variable point coordinates.

Dually, the real number triple (u_1, u_2, u_3) represented a line, and a linear equation in these variables represented a point. The resulting geometry was called real coordinate geometry of the projective plane. However, when number triples thus employed were extended to include complex numbers, there resulted a new system called complex coordinate geometry of the projective plane.

The role of complex geometry in this development will be better understood and appreciated when the metric projective geometries of Part III of the text are discussed.

Chapter 11

TRANSFORMATION THEORY

An outstanding development in geometry since Euclid is the theory resulting from the concept of geometric transformations.   By a transformation, or mapping of the plane on itself, is meant a rule or an operation which assigns, to every point P of the plane, a point P', called the image, or transform, of P.   The process was illustrated in Chap. 5, where to each point P of the Euclidean plane corresponded its inverse point P'.

Another example of a transformation is a rotation of the plane about a fixed point O (Fig. 11.1a).   Here, point P and its transform P' are

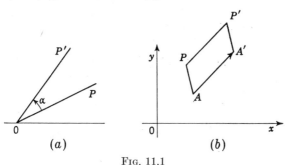

(a) (b)

Fig. 11.1

equidistant from 0, but the angles which OP and OP' make with a fixed direction OX, differ by a constant angle α.

The parallel translations which move every point d units in a given direction $\overline{AA}'$ (Fig. 11.1b) and, more generally, the rigid motions of the plane, which are combinations of rotations and parallel translations, are other familiar illustrations of geometric transformations.

The geometric language used in describing these transformations will now be replaced by the language of algebra.   After this is done, translations and rotations in the Euclidean plane will be linked with transformations in the projective plane.

One of the primary aims of this chapter is an introduction to the Erlanger program, proposed by Klein in 1872, in which geometries are classified by means of their invariants under certain sets of transformations.   This very ingenious program, which is but another example of comprehensive vision in mathematics, has had a profound effect on all subsequent thinking.

11.1. Rigid Motions

For illustrative purposes, and for later generalizations, equations of translation and equations of rotation in the Euclidean plane are reviewed first.   The formula for the distance d between two points $P(x_1,y_1)$ and $P(x_2,y_2)$ of this plane is:

$$d = \sqrt{(x_2 - x_1)^2 + (y_2 - y_1)^2} \tag{1}$$

If equations of two lines of this plane are

$$L_1: \quad a_1x + a_2y + a_3 = 0$$
$$L_2: \quad b_1x + b_2y + b_3 = 0$$

the angle θ between these lines is given by the formula

$$\theta = \cos^{-1} \frac{a_1b_2 + a_2b_1}{\sqrt{a_1{}^2 + a_2{}^2} \sqrt{b_1{}^2 + b_2{}^2}} \tag{2}$$

where all quantities represent real numbers.   Both formulas are used in that which follows.

Equations of translation are obtained by noting first that a translation is completely determined by a directed line segment AA'.   If the translation carries the arbitrary point $P(x,y)$ into the point $P'(x',y')$, and the projections of the segment AA' on the x and y axes are given by the respective real numbers a and b (Fig. 11.2), the equations of translation are

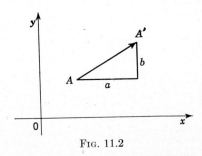

Fig. 11.2

$$x' = x + a$$
$$y' = y + b \tag{3}$$

For arbitrary values of a and b, (3) represents a *set of translations*.
Under the particular translation

$$x' = x + 4$$
$$y' = y - 2 \tag{4}$$

the triangle of Fig. 11.3 having vertices $A(2,0)$, $B(4,1)$, $C(2,1)$ is transformed into the congruent triangle with vertices $A'(6,-2)$, $B'(8,-1)$, $C'(6,-1)$, and to all outward appearances the original triangle has simply been moved to the new position $A'B'C'$ without any change of size or shape. Such a motion, in the case of physical objects, is called a rigid motion, and hence modern geometers have combined the concept of motion with that of a transformation by calling (3) equations of rigid motions.

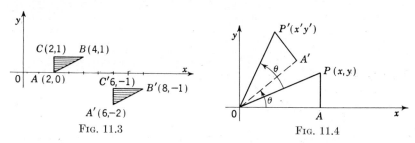

FIG. 11.3   FIG. 11.4

If a transformation is not a translation, but a rotation about the origin, equations of rotation may be obtained as follows:

Let point $P(x,y)$ be rotated about the origin O through the given angle θ into the point $P'(x',y')$ (Fig. 11.4). If OA is the projection of OP on the x axis and if A' is the transform of point A under the rotation, then

$$OA = OA' = x$$
$$AP = A'P' = y \tag{5}$$

and a well-known property of projection gives the relation

$$\text{proj } OP' = \text{proj } OA' + \text{proj } A'P' \tag{6}$$

Since the projections of OP', OA', and $A'P'$ on the x axis are, respectively, x', $x \cos \theta$, and $-y \sin \theta$, substitution of these values in (6) gives

$$x' = x \cos \theta - y \sin \theta$$

Similarly, projection on the y axis gives

$$y' = x \sin \theta + y \cos \theta$$

and thus the equations of rotation are

$$x' = x \cos \theta - y \sin \theta$$
$$y' = x \sin \theta + y \cos \theta \tag{7}$$

[If the rotation is about the point (x_0,y_0) through the angle θ, the equations of rotation are

$$x' - x_0 = (x - x_0)\cos\theta - (y - y_0)\sin\theta$$
$$y' - y_0 = (x - x_0)\sin\theta + (y - y_0)\cos\theta$$
$$(8)$$

(see Exercise 3 below).]

Under the particular rotation

$$x' = \frac{x - y}{\sqrt{2}}$$
$$y' = \frac{x + y}{\sqrt{2}}$$
$$(9)$$

the triangle ABC of Fig. 11.5 is transformed into the congruent triangle with vertices at the following points:

$$\bar{A}(\sqrt{2},\sqrt{2}) \qquad \bar{B}(\tfrac{3}{2}\sqrt{2},\tfrac{5}{2}\sqrt{2}) \qquad \bar{C}(\tfrac{1}{2}\sqrt{2},\tfrac{3}{2}\sqrt{2})$$

as shown in the same figure. Again, the particular transformation has

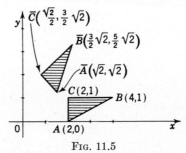

Fig. 11.5

effected a change of position of the original figure without a change of size or shape. It too is called a rigid motion.

EXERCISES

1. Draw the transform of triangle ABC (Fig. 11.3) under the transformation

$$x' = 2\left(x\cos\frac{\pi}{4} - y\sin\frac{\pi}{4}\right)$$
$$y' = 2\left(x\sin\frac{\pi}{4} + y\cos\frac{\pi}{4}\right)$$

2. Show that the equations

$$x' = r(x\cos\theta - y\sin\theta)$$
$$y' = r(x\sin\theta + y\cos\theta) \qquad r \neq 0$$

represent a transformation which involves a uniform enlargement or reduction of size. (It is called a similarity transformation.)

3. Derive Eqs. (8), Section 11.1.

11.2. Reflections and Rigid Motions

Both translations and rotations preserved distance between points, and a natural question to ask now is: Are there other transformations in the plane with this same property?

It is interesting to note in this connection that a distance-preserving transformation which sends two given points $A(4,1)$ and $B(7,4)$ (Fig. 11.6) into the respective points $A'(2,5)$, $B'(-1,8)$ may be obtained by *two successive reflections* as follows:

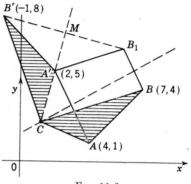

Let B_1 (Fig. 11.6) be the reflection of point B in the perpendicular bisector of AA'. Then $AB = A'B_1$ (Why?), and since by hypothesis $AB = A'B'$, the perpendicular bisector of B_1B' passes through A'. A second reflection in

FIG. 11.6

this latter bisector, $A'M$, will therefore send point B_1 into B', and the first reflection, followed by the second, sends the given points A, B into the points A', B', so that the distance AB equals the distance $A'B'$.

It will now be shown that this same result could have been obtained by rotation about the point C of meeting of the perpendicular bisectors of line segments AA' and BB'.

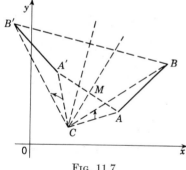

FIG. 11.7

In the triangles ABC and $A'B'C$, $AC = A'C$, and $BC = B'C$ (Why?). Since by hypothesis $AB = A'B'$, the two triangles are congruent, and hence

$$\angle ACB = \angle A'CB'$$

Addition of $\angle BCA'$ to each of these angles then gives the result

$$\angle ACA' = \angle BCB' = \phi$$

and hence rotation about C through the angle ϕ transforms points A, B into points A', B'.

These same arguments are valid for any two points A, B and their transforms A', B' (Fig. 11.7) when distance $AB =$ distance $A'B'$ and line AB is not parallel to line $A'B'$. If lines AA' and BB' are parallel, B' may take either one of the two positions B_1' or B_2' (Fig. 11.8). In the former case, a single rotation about the point C of meeting of lines AB and $A'B_1'$ effects the desired transformation. In the latter case, a single translation through a distance AA' in the direction of the directed line segment AA' gives the desired result.

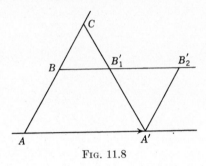

FIG. 11.8

Since a rigid motion is completely determined by two pairs of corresponding points [28, p. 89], proof has been given of the theorem:

Theorem 11.1

A rigid motion is either a translation or a rotation.

EXERCISES

1. Using the theory of Sec. 11.2, find the equations of rigid motion sending the points $A(4,2)$ and $B(3,5)$ into the respective points $A'(2,4)$ and $B'(-1,5)$. *Hint:* Find point $C(x_0,y_0)$ of meeting of lines AA' and BB'. Then, use Eqs. (8), Sec. 11.1.

2. (a) Show that the equations which transform points $A(4,1)$ and $B(7,4)$ into the respective points $A'(2,5)$ and $B'(-1,8)$ are given by

$$x' = -y + 3$$
$$y' = x + 1$$

(b) Do these equations represent a translation? A rotation? Why?

3. (a) Plot the lines

$$L_1: \quad y = 0 \qquad L_2: \quad y = x$$

and their transforms L_1', L_2' under the rigid motion

$$x' = x \cos 30° - y \sin 30° + 1$$
$$y' = x \sin 30° + y \cos 30° - 1$$

(b) Show that the angle between L_1' and L_2' equals the angle between L_1 and L_2.

11.3. Product Transformations

If T_1 is a transformation which sends the point $P(x,y)$ into the point $P'(x',y')$ and if T_2 is a transformation which sends point $P'(x',y')$ into a third point $P''(x'', y'')$, the transformation T_1 followed by T_2 is a transformation which sends the first point P directly into the third point P'' and is called the *product of the two transformations.* It is denoted by the symbol $T_1 T_2$.

Equations of the product $T_1 T_2$ for the respective transformations

$$T_1: \quad \begin{aligned} x' &= x + 1 \\ y' &= y + 2 \end{aligned} \tag{1}$$

and
$$T_2: \quad \begin{aligned} x' &= x + 2 \\ y' &= y - 3 \end{aligned} \tag{2}$$

are

$$T_1 T_2: \quad \begin{aligned} x'' &= x' + 2 = (x + 1) + 2 = x + 3 \\ y'' &= y' - 3 = (y + 2) - 3 = y - 1 \end{aligned} \tag{3}$$

Under the transformation T_1 the point $P(2,1)$ (Fig. 11.9) goes into the point $P'(3,3)$, and under T_2 point $P'(3,3)$ goes into the point $P''(5,0)$. The product $T_1 T_2$, there-fore, sends the point $P(2,1)$ directly into the point $P''(5,0)$.

Another example of a product of two transformations is a rotation followed by a translation. When a rotation about the origin through the angle θ is followed by a trans-lation in a direction whose compo-

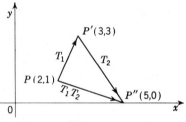

Fig. 11.9

nents are a and b, the product transformation is given by the equations

$$\begin{aligned} x' &= x \cos \theta - y \sin \theta + a \\ y' &= x \sin \theta + y \cos \theta + b \end{aligned} \tag{4}$$

An analytic proof will be given shortly that this transformation pre-serves both size and shape of figures and hence represents a rigid motion. Equations (4) are called, therefore, *the general equations of rigid motion.*

Order is again an essential feature of the definition of a product. For example, if T is the translation T_1 of this section and R the rota-tion (9) of Sec. 11.1, the product RT is

$$RT: \quad x'' = x' + 1 = \frac{x - y}{\sqrt{2}} + 1 = \frac{\sqrt{2}}{2}(x - y + \sqrt{2})$$

$$y'' = y' + 2 = \frac{x + y}{\sqrt{2}} + 1 = \frac{\sqrt{2}}{2}(x + y + \sqrt{2})$$

whereas the product RT is

$$TR: \quad x'' = \frac{\bar{x} - \bar{y}}{\sqrt{2}} = \frac{(x + 1) - (y + 2)}{\sqrt{2}} = \frac{\sqrt{2}}{2}(x - y - 1)$$

$$y'' = \frac{\bar{x} + \bar{y}}{\sqrt{2}} = \frac{(x + 1) + (y + 2)}{\sqrt{2}} = \frac{\sqrt{2}}{2}(x + y + 3)$$

Thus, in general, the product T_iT_j is not the same as the product T_jT_i. When these two products are the same, so that

$$T_iT_j = T_jT_i$$

the product is said to be commutative.

EXERCISES

1. If T_1 and T_2 are the respective transformations

$$
\begin{aligned}
T_1: \quad & x' = x - 2 \\
& y' = y + 1 \\
T_2: \quad & x' = -y \\
& y' = -x
\end{aligned}
$$

is $T_1T_2 = T_2T_1$? Give reasons for your answer.

2. Is the product of a rotation R followed by a translation T commutative? Illustrate and prove your answer.

11.4. The Inverse and Identity Transformations

By the inverse of a transformation T_i, if the inverse exists, is meant the transformation which sends the transformed point back to its original position and hence nullifies the effect of the original transformation. It is denoted by the symbol T_i^{-1}.

For example, if T_i is the translation sending a point a given distance in a given direction, its inverse T_i^{-1} is a translation which sends the transformed point the given distance in the reverse direction.

The product $T_iT_i^{-1}$ of a transformation by its inverse is the identity transformation I given by the equations

$$
\begin{aligned}
I: \quad & x' = x \\
& y' = y
\end{aligned}
$$

which leave every point of the plane fixed. It is written symbolically

$$T_iT_i^{-1} = I$$

in accordance with the laws of algebra.

11.5. Groups

A distinction is made now between a set and a group of transformations. The two words are often used interchangeably in everyday life, as when one speaks of a set, or a group, of people. In mathematics, however, the word group has a very different meaning, which will now be explained.

A set of transformations such that each transformation of the set has an inverse is, by definition, a group, if the set has the following properties:

Property 1

The product of every two transformations of the set belongs to the set.

Property 2

The inverse of every transformation of the set belongs to the set.

Since the product of a transformation by its inverse is the identity transformation, it follows from property 1 that *every group contains the identity transformation.*

The set of translations in the plane:

$$\begin{aligned} x' &= x + a_i \\ y' &= y + b_i \end{aligned} \qquad i = 1, \ldots, n \qquad (1)$$

form a group. To prove this statement, it must be shown that the product of any two transformations of the set belongs to the set and also that the inverse of any transformation of the set is a member of the set.

Now, the product of any two translations T_i and T_j of (1) is the transformation

$$T_i T_j : \quad \begin{aligned} \bar{x} &= x' + a_j = x + a_i + a_j = x + c_i \\ \bar{y} &= y' + b_j = y + b_i + b_j = y + d_i \end{aligned}$$

which belongs to the set. Also, the inverse of any transformation of the set is the transformation:

$$\bar{x}' = x - a_i \qquad \bar{y}' = y - b_i$$

which also belongs to the set. Thus (1) forms a group.

In a similar manner, it can be shown that the rigid-motion equations, Eqs. (4), Sec. 11.3, form a group (see Exercise 2a, Sec. 11.6).

11.6. Subgroups

If any subset of a group of transformations forms a group, *the subset is called a subgroup of the original group.* For example, the set of transformations

$$I: \quad x' = x \qquad y' = y$$
$$T: \quad x' = -x \qquad y' = -y$$

consisting of the identity transformation I and the rotation T through an angle $\theta = 180°$ form a subgroup of the group of rotations in the plane. This is so, because the inverse of each of these transformations is the same transformation and hence belongs to the set. Also

$$IT = T = TI$$

The product of any two transformations of the set therefore belongs to the set, and hence the set forms a group.

EXERCISES

1. Show that the four transformations

$$T_1: \quad x' = x \qquad y' = y$$
$$T_2: \quad x' = -y \qquad y' = x$$
$$T_3: \quad x' = -x \qquad y' = -y$$
$$T_4: \quad x' = y \qquad y' = -x$$

form a group.

2. Show that each of the following sets of transformations forms a group: (a) the rigid motions, (b) the similarity transformations.

11.7. Invariants

By a geometric invariant of a group of transformations is meant a property of a figure which is unchanged under all transformations of the group. For example, distance is an invariant of the group of rigid motions, as is the angle between any two lines. Analytic proofs of these statements follow.

Let $P_1(x_1,y_1)$ and $P_2(x_2,y_2)$ be any two points of the Euclidean plane, in which the distance d between the two points is given by formula (1), Sec. 11.1. If $P_1'(x_1',y_1')$ and $P_2'(x_2',y_2')$ are their respective transforms under the general transformations of rigid motion, Eqs. (4), Sec. 11.3, then

$$x_2' - x_1' = (x_2 - x_1) \cos \theta - (y_2 - y_1) \sin \theta \qquad (1)$$
$$y_2' - y_1' = (x_2 - x_1) \sin \theta + (y_2 - y_1) \cos \theta \qquad (2)$$

from which it follows that

$$(x_2' - x_1')^2 + (y_2' - y_1')^2 = (x_2 - x_1)^2 + (y_2 - y_1)^2 \qquad (3)$$

and hence the square of the distance between the transformed points P_1' and P_2' equals the square of the distance d between the original points. Thus proof has been given of the following theorem:

Theorem 11.2

Distance is an invariant of rigid motion.

An expression such as

$$(x_2 - x_1)^2 + (y_2 - y_1)^2$$

which equals the same expression in coordinates of the transformed points is called an *algebraic* invariant of the points (x_1,y_1) and (x_2,y_2).

To prove the invariance of the angle θ between two lines L_1 and L_2, let equations of these lines and their transforms L_1' and L_2' be

$$L_1: \quad a_1x + a_2y + a_3 = 0 \qquad L_1': \quad a_1'x' + a_2'y' + a_3' = 0$$
$$L_2: \quad b_1x + b_2y + b_3 = 0 \qquad L_2': \quad b_1'x' + b_2'y' + b_3' = 0$$

Then, a simple calculation (see Exercise 2 below) gives

$$\frac{a_1'b_2' - a_2'b_1'}{a_1'b_1' + a_2'b_2'} = \frac{a_1b_2 - a_2b_1}{a_1b_1 + a_2b_2} \tag{4}$$

Since the left-hand side of this equation is the tangent of the angle θ' between the transformed lines and the right-hand side is the tangent of the angle θ between the original lines, proof has been given of the theorem:

Theorem 11.3

The angle between two lines is an invariant of rigid motion.

EXERCISES

1. Show that the expression $\Delta = x_1y_2 - x_2y_1$ is an algebraic invariant of the points (x_1,y_1), (x_2,y_2). What does the expression represent geometrically?

2. Verify Eq. (4) above.

11.8. Linear One-dimensional Transformations

The present objective is to show that the elementary transformations studied thus far are only special cases of a much larger group which express in algebraic language the 1-1 correspondences established by projections.

By way of introducing this new class of transformations, a study is made of the particular transformation

$$x' = \frac{2(x - 1)}{x + 2} \tag{1}$$

which establishes a 1-1 correspondence between points $P(x)$ of a line L and points $P'(x')$ of another line L' (or the same line), so that to a real point of one line corresponds a real point of the other. It is called a *real* transformation in accordance with the definition:

A transformation of a form of the complex plane S' is said to be real if it transforms each real element of the form into a real element of another (or the same) form.

Only *real* transformations are considered in what follows. Under transformation (1) the three particular points $P_1(1)$, $P_2(4)$, $P_3(7)$ of a line L (Fig. 11.10) are transformed into the respective points $P_1'(0)$, $P_2'(1)$, $P_3'(\frac{4}{3})$ of a line L'.

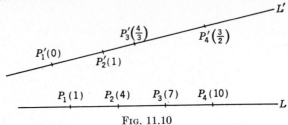

Fᴵɢ. 11.10

A fourth point $P_4(10)$ of line L then has for its transform the point $P_4'(\frac{3}{2})$ of line L', and a simple calculation for the cross ratios (P_1P_2, P_3P_4) and $(P_1'P_2', P_3'P_4')$ of these points gives

$$(P_1P_2, P_3P_4) = \frac{(7-1)(4-10)}{(4-7)(10-1)} = \frac{4}{3}$$

$$(P_1'P_2', P_3'P_4') = \frac{(\frac{4}{3}-0)(1-\frac{3}{2})}{(1-\frac{4}{3})(\frac{3}{2}-0)} = \frac{4}{3}$$

Transformation (1) has therefore preserved the cross ratio (P_1P_2, P_3P_4) of the original four points.

Suppose now that a cross-ratio-preserving transformation is desired which sends the three given points $P_1(1)$, $P_2(4)$, $P_3(7)$ into the respective points $P_1'(0)$, $P_2'(1)$, $P_3'(\frac{4}{3})$. How can this transformation be obtained?

To answer this question, let $P_4'(x')$ be the transform of $P_4(x)$ under the desired transformation. Then, the coordinates x_i and x_i' of the points $P_i(x)$ and $P_i'(x')$ must, by formula (2) of Sec. 10.8 satisfy the relation

$$\frac{(x_3' - x_1')(x_4' - x_2')}{(x_3' - x_2')(x_4' - x_1')} = \frac{(x_3 - x_1)(x_4 - x_2)}{(x_3 - x_2)(x_4 - x_1)} \qquad (2)$$

Upon substitution in (2) of the values

$$x_1 = 1 \qquad x_2 = 4 \qquad x_3 = 7 \qquad x_4 = x$$
and
$$x_1' = 0 \qquad x_2' = 1 \qquad x_3' = \tfrac{4}{3} \qquad x_4' = x'$$

there results the transformation

$$x' = \frac{2(x-1)}{x+2}$$

which is identical with (1).

It is seen therefore that (1) has preserved cross ratio and also that a transformation which sends three given real points of a line L into three points of a line L' is a linear transformation. Furthermore, when lines L and L' are so placed that $P_1(1)$ coincides with its transformed point $P_1'(0)$, the intersection C of lines $P_2 P_2'$ and $P_3 P_3'$ (Fig. 11.11) is the center of a projection which sets up a 1-1 correspondence between points of lines L and L'. Since cross ratio is preserved on projection, the point X in which line CP_4 meets L' must be the point $P'(\frac{3}{2})$ already determined from (1) as the transform of $P_4(10)$.

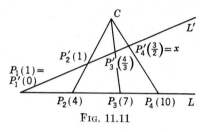

Fig. 11.11

Thus, the transform of point P_4 may be obtained, either by the use of Eq. (1) or by a geometric construction. Whether one uses geometric or algebraic tools is immaterial, but certainly at the start of this investigation it was not known that (1) was simply a projection expressed in algebraic language.

Transformations given by (1) are now called *projective* transformations, in accordance with the definition:

A correspondence between two pencils of points which is 1-1 and preserves cross ratio is a projective correspondence, and transformations given by projective correspondences are called projective transformations.

Consider next the more general set of transformations

$$x' = \frac{a_{11}x + a_{12}}{a_{21}x + a_{22}}$$

or

$$\rho x_1' = a_{11}x_1 + a_{12}t$$
$$\rho t' = a_{21}x_1 + a_{22}t$$

(3)

where the a_{ij}'s are real numbers subject to the condition

$$\begin{vmatrix} a_{11} & a_{12} \\ a_{21} & a_{22} \end{vmatrix} \neq 0$$

and where ρ is an arbitrary complex constant, $\neq 0$. The factor ρ takes care of the fact that substitution of a particular set of coordinates from among the many possible sets which represent a point will give some pair of coordinates for the transformed point.

By arguments very similar to those just given for the particular transformation (1), it is possible to show that transformations of the set (3) preserve cross ratio; and, conversely, every transformation which sends three given real points of a line into three given real points of another, or the same, line and which also preserves cross ratio is of the form (3). Proofs of these statements may be found in the literature [28, pp. 95–102].

Because the projective transformations (3) are linear in the variables and also because they transform points of a line into points of a line, they are called *linear one-dimensional transformations*. It is not difficult to show that they form a group (see Exercise 4 below).

EXERCISES

1. The equation

$$x' = \frac{x + 3}{x - 1}$$

represents a projective transformation of a line into itself. Show that it leaves each of the points $x = 3$ and $x = -1$ fixed in position.

2. If a line is carried into itself by the linear transformation

$$x' = \frac{3x + 2}{x + 4}$$

prove that two points A, B of the line remain fixed and that every other point P and its transform divide these fixed points in a constant cross ratio.

3. Find the equation of the projective transformation which carries the points $A(0)$, $B(1)$, $C(2)$ of a line L into the respective points $A'(-1)$, $B'(0)$, $C'(2)$ of a second line L'.

4. Prove that transformations (3) of this section have the group property.

11.9. Linear Two-dimensional Transformations

The extension of the foregoing theory to points in the complex plane is a lengthy process, but the results can be anticipated and summarized as follows:

The general linear transformation of real points of a projective plane K into real points of a projective plane K' is, in homogeneous coordinates,

$$\begin{aligned}
\rho x'_1 &= a_{11}x_1 + a_{12}x_2 + a_{13}x_3 \\
\rho x'_2 &= a_{21}x_1 + a_{22}x_2 + a_{23}x_3 \\
\rho x'_3 &= a_{31}x_1 + a_{32}x_2 + a_{33}x_3
\end{aligned} \tag{1}$$

where ρ is an arbitrary complex number $\neq 0$ and the a_{ij}'s are real constants subject to the condition

$$\begin{vmatrix} a_{11} & a_{12} & a_{13} \\ a_{21} & a_{22} & a_{23} \\ a_{31} & a_{32} & a_{33} \end{vmatrix} = |a_{ij}| \neq 0$$

Because these equations are linear in the variables and also because they transform points of a plane into points of a plane, they are called *linear two-dimensional transformations.* Because they transform points into points and lines into lines, they are also called *collineations.*

As in the one-dimensional case, linear two-dimensional real transformations are projective transformations. Proofs that they form a group and also preserve cross ratio may be found in the literature [28, pp. 105–109].

11.10. Rigid Motions from a Projective Viewpoint

For special values of the constants, the two-dimensional projective transformations given by Eqs. (1) of the last section reduce, in non-homogeneous coordinates, to the well-known transformations of rigid motion in the Euclidean plane:

$$\begin{aligned} x' &= x \cos \theta - y \sin \theta + a \\ y' &= x \sin \theta + y \cos \theta + b \end{aligned} \tag{1}$$

where the constants a, b, and θ are real numbers.

Since distance and angle concepts have not yet been introduced into the projective plane, no metric significance can be attached to (1) until these concepts are defined. However, they will be called rigid motions in the projective plane, with the understanding that, at this point, the name serves only to distinguish this particular set of projective transformations from others of the group of linear two-dimensional projective transformations given by Eq. (1), Sec. 11.9.

A particularly significant fact concerning these rigid motions is stated in the next theorem:

Theorem 11.4

Every rigid motion carries each of the circular points at infinity $I(1,i,0)$, $J(1,-i,0)$ into itself.

To prove the theorem, it is noted first that, in homogeneous coordinates, Eqs. (1) become:

$$\begin{aligned} \rho x_1' &= x_1 \cos \theta - x_2 \sin \theta + ax_3 \\ \rho x_2' &= x_1 \sin \theta + x_2 \cos \theta + bx_3 \\ \rho x_3' &= x_3 \end{aligned} \tag{2}$$

where ρ is a constant $\neq 0$.   Their effect on the point $I(1,i,0)$ is seen by substituting the values

$$x_1 = 1 \qquad x_2 = i \qquad x_3 = 0$$

in (2).   There result the equations

$$\begin{aligned} \rho x_1' &= \cos \theta - i \sin \theta \\ \rho x_2' &= \sin \theta + i \cos \theta = i(\cos \theta - i \sin \theta) \\ \rho x_3' &= 0 \end{aligned} \qquad (3)$$

which, for $\rho = \cos \theta - i \sin \theta$, are satisfied by

$$x_1' = 1 \qquad x_2' = i \qquad x_3' = 0$$

Hence (2) transforms the point $I(1,i,0)$ into itself.   Similarly, the same transformation (2) transforms the point $J(1,-i,0)$ into itself, and the theorem is proved.

Since the circular points at infinity, $I(1,i,0)$ and $J(1,-i,0)$, determine the line $x_3 = 0$, an immediate consequence of this theorem is:

Corollary

The line $x_3 = 0$ is an invariant of rigid motion.

Now that rigid motions have been seen to have the circular points at infinity, I, J, as invariants, one might reasonably inquire whether this latter property completely characterizes such transformations.   In other words, is every projective transformation which has I and J as invariants a rigid motion?

This question cannot be answered in the affirmative.   Instead, it will be shown that projective transformations which leave each of the circular points at infinity fixed are transformations of similarity and hence are not necessarily rigid motions.

11.11. Similarity Transformations from a Projective Viewpoint

If the projective transformations (collineations)

$$\begin{aligned} \rho x_1' &= a_{11}x_1 + a_{12}x_2 + a_{13}x_3 \\ \rho x_2' &= a_{21}x_1 + a_{22}x_2 + a_{23}x_3 \qquad |a_{ij}| \neq 0 \\ \rho x_3' &= a_{31}x_1 + a_{32}x_2 + a_{33}x_3 \end{aligned} \qquad (1)$$

have $I(1,i,0)$ and $J(1,-i,0)$ as invariants, they carry the line $x_3 = 0$ of these points into the line $x_3' = 0$, and hence

$$a_{31} = a_{32} = 0 \qquad \text{and} \qquad a_{33} \neq 0$$

Division of each of Eqs. (1) by a_{33} then gives

$$\begin{aligned}
\sigma x_1' &= a_1 x_1 + a_2 x_2 + a_3 x_3 \\
\sigma x_2' &= b_1 x_1 + b_2 x_2 + b_3 x_3 \\
\sigma x_3' &= \qquad\qquad\qquad\quad x_3
\end{aligned} \tag{2}$$

where, for convenience,

$$\sigma = \frac{\rho}{a_{33}} \qquad \frac{a_{1i}}{a_{33}} = a_i \qquad \frac{a_{2i}}{a_{33}} = b_i \qquad i = 1, 2, 3$$

Since $|a_{ij}| \neq 0$,

$$\begin{vmatrix} a_1 & a_2 \\ b_1 & b_2 \end{vmatrix} \neq 0 \tag{3}$$

and since (2) is to carry each of the points $I(1, i, 0)$ and $J(1, -i, 0)$ into itself,

$$\begin{aligned}
\sigma_1 &= a_1 - i a_2 \qquad & \sigma_2 &= a_1 + i a_2 \\
-i\sigma_1 &= b_1 - i b_2 \qquad & i\sigma_2 &= b_1 + i b_2
\end{aligned}$$

where σ_1 and σ_2 are constants $\neq 0$. Therefore

$$\begin{aligned}
i a_1 + a_2 + b_1 - i b_2 &= 0 \\
-i a_1 + a_2 + b_1 + i b_2 &= 0
\end{aligned}$$

and hence

$$a_2 = -b_1 \qquad b_2 = a_1 \tag{4}$$

Substitution of these results in (2) then gives

$$\begin{aligned}
\rho x_1' &= a_1 x_1 - b_1 x_2 + a_3 x_3 \\
\rho x_2' &= b_1 x_1 + a_1 x_2 + b_3 x_3 \\
\rho x_3' &= \qquad\qquad\qquad\quad x_3
\end{aligned} \tag{5}$$

which in nonhomogeneous coordinates become

$$\begin{aligned}
x' &= a_1 x - b_1 y + a_3 \\
y' &= b_1 x + a_1 y + b_3
\end{aligned} \tag{6}$$

But, from (3) and (4),

$$a_1^2 + b_1^2 \neq 0$$

and hence, if $r^2 = a_1^2 + b_1^2$, it is possible to set

$$\begin{aligned}
\frac{a_1}{r} &= \cos\theta \qquad & \frac{b_1}{r} &= \sin\theta \\
\frac{a_3}{r} &= a \qquad & \frac{b_3}{r} &= b
\end{aligned} \tag{7}$$

and reduce (6) to the form

$$x' = r(x \cos \theta - y \sin \theta + a)$$
$$y' = r(x \sin \theta + y \cos \theta + b) \qquad r \neq 0 \qquad (8)$$

But these equations represent similarity transformations in the Euclidean plane. Proof has therefore been given of the following theorem:

Theorem 11.5

The transformations of similarity are collineations which have the circular points at infinity as invariants.

Now, if (8) carries the points (x_1, y_1), (x_2, y_2) into the respective points (x'_1, y'_1), (x'_2, y'_2),

$$(x'_2 - x'_1)^2 + (y'_2 - y'_1)^2 = r^2[(x_2 - x_1)^2 + (y_2 - y_1)^2] \qquad (9)$$

and since, for $r = 1$, (8) reduces to the transformations of rigid motion, it is seen that the expression

$$(x_2 - x_1)^2 + (y_2 - y_1)^2 \qquad (10)$$

is an algebraic invariant of the latter transformations.

Remark

In elementary coordinate geometry, the expression (10) is the square of the *distance* between the two points (x_1, y_1) and (x_2, y_2), and in the plane the real conic

$$x_1^2 + x_2^2 + a_1 x_1 x_3 + a_2 x_2 x_3 + a_3 x_3^2 = 0$$

is a *circle*. It is easily verified (see Exercise 1 below) that this equation is satisfied by the points $I(1, i, 0)$, $J(1, -i, 0)$.

Conversely, if the real conic

$$A x_1^2 + B x_1 x_2 + C x_2^2 + D x_1 x_3 + E x_2 x_3 + F x_3^2 = 0$$

contains these points, then

$$A - Bi - C = 0 \qquad A + Bi - C = 0$$

from which it follows, if A, B, C are not all zero, that

$$A = C \qquad B = 0$$

and the conic is a circle.

It is for these reasons that the conjugate complex points $I(1, i, 0)$, $J(1, -i, 0)$ are called the *circular points at infinity*.

EXERCISES

1. Prove that the points $I(1,i,0)$, $J(1,-i,0)$ are on the real conic

$$x_1{}^2 + x_2{}^2 + a_1x_1x_3 + a_2x_2x_3 + a_3x_3{}^2 = 0$$

2. (a) Prove that the collineation:

$$x' = \frac{x}{2x - 1} \qquad y' = \frac{y}{2x - 1}$$

leaves the origin O and each point of the line $x = 1$ fixed and carries any other point P into its harmonic conjugate with respect to O and the point in which OP meets $x = 1$.   (b) Show that the collineation is its own inverse.

3. Find the equation of the line L into which the line $y - 6 = 0$ is carried by the collineation

$$x' = \frac{3x + y + 4}{y - 1} \qquad y' = \frac{-4x - y + 1}{y - 1}$$

and show that the given transformation preserves the expression (10) above.

4. Given the transformation

$$x' = \frac{x}{3x - 2} \qquad y' = \frac{y}{3x - 2}$$

(a) What points are fixed under the transformation?   (b) Find its inverse.   (c) Is the transformation a rigid motion?   Give reasons for your answer.

5. Determine the collineation which leaves each of the real points $(1,1,0)$ and $(1,-1,0)$ fixed.   Is the algebraic expression (10) above an invariant of your transformation?   Give reasons for your answer.

6. Show that the equations

$$x' = \frac{r^2x}{x^2 + y^2} \qquad y' = \frac{r^2y}{x^2 + y^2}$$

represent in the Euclidean plane an inversion in the circle with radius r and center at the origin of the xy coordinate system.

11.12. The Erlanger Program.   Concluding Remarks

As mentioned earlier, one goal of this chapter is an introduction to the Erlanger program, which classifies geometries on the basis of the content or character of theorems rather than on the method used in obtaining them.

The program begins with the formal definition:

A geometry is defined by a group G of transformations when its definitions and theorems deal with properties of figures invariant under transformations of G but not invariant under transformations of any other group containing G.

Thus projective geometry is defined by the group of all projective collineations in the plane, since definitions and theorems of this geometry express properties which are invariant under this group. Many of these projective properties are also invariant under more restricted subgroups, such as that of rigid motions. But the system which studies properties invariant under *rigid motion* is Euclidean geometry, and hence, in the Erlanger program, *Euclidean geometry is a special subdivision of projective geometry.* (Strictly speaking, Euclid's elementary system is a mixture of several geometries in the sense of the definition just given. In the theory of similar figures, it takes account only of shape; in the theory of congruent figures, it is concerned also with size. Taken as a whole, it is a study of properties of figures unchanged under rigid motion, for it is only with respect to rigid motion that all properties studied are preserved.)

The classification goes much further. When a *real* conic, called the *absolute*, has been chosen in the projective plane, the group of all collineations leaving this conic invariant is called the *hyperbolic metric* group, and the study of properties of figures unchanged under this group is *hyperbolic non-Euclidean geometry.*

When the absolute conic is *imaginary*, the group of projective transformations leaving this conic invariant is the *elliptic metric* group, and the resulting geometry is *elliptic non-Euclidean geometry.*

Occupying an intermediate position between these geometries is a third system in which the absolute conic degenerates into the line $x_3 = 0$ of the plane taken twice. Projective transformations leaving this line invariant have just been shown to be similarity transformations, which include rigid motions. The study of properties of figures unchanged under rigid motion is parabolic geometry, the system which extends and generalizes Euclid.

All three of these geometries, parabolic, hyperbolic, and elliptic will be studied in more detail in Part Three of this text.

Part Three

NON-EUCLIDEAN AND
METRIC PROJECTIVE GEOMETRIES

Chapter 12

EARLY AXIOMATIC THEORIES AND THE LATER METRIC APPROACH TO NON-EUCLIDEAN GEOMETRY

By a metric geometry is meant one in which distance and angle concepts are defined. These concepts, which, incidentally, are used in elementary geometry but never clearly defined there, have not as yet been introduced into the formal treatment of projective geometry as presented in Part Two of this text. But they must be included now if projective geometry is to be viewed as the over-all science which encompasses the elementary system of Euclid and the equally famous non-Euclidean geometries whose discovery startled a phlegmatic and complacent world.

As so often happens in mathematics, two mathematical theories, projective geometry on the one hand and non-Euclidean geometry on the other hand, were developed quite independently of each other, and only much later was the connection between them discovered. Initially, non-Euclidean geometry was a modification of Euclid, and projective geometry was a collection of certain isolated theorems of Euclid.

The obvious desire to link these detached systems inspired the new *projective metric theories*, which brought Euclidean, non-Euclidean, and projective geometry together into one organic whole and inspired Cayley's succinct (and already quoted) exclamation, "Projective geometry is all geometry." This unification process is a monument to the imagination and logical power of the human mind.

Before the new metric theories and their great unifying power are discussed, some of the early non-Euclidean theories which inspired them will be examined. To study either type of theory without knowledge of the other is to read a story only half told.

Any account of the discovery, rise, and development of non-Euclidean geometry reads like fiction. It is a completely absorbing tale of struggle, hardship, early defeat, and final success. When the story is finished, the reader will see for himself how much the world is indebted to the men whose insight, skill, and vision brought unity into a vast collection of detached and apparently isolated theories. Quietly, steadily, and with determination, the early workers went about their colossal task of revising Euclid.

12.1. Some Kantian Philosophy

Late in the seventeenth century, when physicists were laying the foundations to be used by later workers in the colossal task of splitting the atom and creating a hydrogen bomb, mathematicians were still attempting to create new geometries. Newton's laws and Euclidean geometry seemed fixed and unalterable; the Kantian philosophy of space was dominating the world; and progress was stymied.

In Kant's philosophy, space was regarded as something already existing in the mind, not a concept resulting from external experience. To be sure, Kant granted that knowledge of space could be obtained directly from experience, but he insisted that certain a priori knowledge was obtained by the mind *independently of experience.*

Mathematical entities, too, were considered to exist in a realm of pure intuition, and mathematical facts or theorems were regarded simply as statements describing existing realities in this realm. In fact, the existence of mathematical truths was the core of Kant's philosophy. Such a simple statement as "the straight line is the shortest distance between two points" was supposed to be a truth coming from a priori judgment. Also, since space originated in the mind, this axiom and others of Euclid were at once acceptable. Theorems were then but logical implications of these axioms, and yet they were at the same time supposed to describe the world of sense perceptions. Some of the arguments were certainly weak.

Fortunately, there were those who detected the weakness of such arguments, but for a long time these critics were unable to gain any general support. As history shows, traditional habits of thought, stressed from infancy, are virtually impregnable walls, withstanding for long sieges the assaults of advanced thinkers. Eventually, however, the walls were weakened by pressure from all sides, and the world was forced to discard outmoded, erroneous beliefs.

In the nineteenth century, to the amazement of the scientific world, if not of the entire world, it was proved conclusively that there could be geometries other than that of Euclid. These new systems, now called non-Euclidean geometries, in turn opened new pathways for science and demonstrated again what can be accomplished by man in his search for eternal truth.

Looking back, one wonders why non-Euclidean geometry was so long in coming. Still, as just indicated, accepted beliefs are hard to dethrone.

12.2. Attempts to Prove Euclid's Parallel Axiom

If there is any one source to which the discovery of non-Euclidean geometry can be attributed, it is to the extensive studies and investigations of Euclid's axioms. Two of the latter are of an essentially different nature from the others: his parallel axiom, frequently called the fifth postulate, and the axiom that a straight line is infinite in extent. Both involve an infinite concept and are, therefore, not experimentally verifiable. How, for instance, can one show by an experiment that a line is infinite in extent, when physical lines like stretched strings or rays of light always have finite length?

Because all the other axioms have a finite character and were suggested by their correspondence with physical objects, early geometers were led to investigate the question of whether or not the parallel axiom was dependent on the others. If so, it could be proved and, hence, would be a theorem, not an axiom, of the system.

Today, anyone who attempts to prove Euclid's parallel axiom is as much out of style as angle trisectors or circle squarers. In Euclid's day, however, and for hundreds of years thereafter, the brains and skill of the mathematical world were engaged in this problem.

Early investigators were, of course, hampered by Kant's philosophy and by the prevailing incorrect beliefs about the nature of space. That is why these investigators directed their efforts toward proving the dependence of the parallel axiom on the other axioms, rather than toward building geometries in which this axiom is denied.

One of the first attempts at a dependence proof was made by Proclus, a commentator on Euclid. He thought that he was dispensing with the parallel axiom when he defined the parallel to a given line as the locus of points at a given distance from the line. However, this merely shifted the difficulty, for it was then necessary to prove that the locus of such points was a straight line. Failing to do so, Proclus had to accept this fact as an axiom, and nothing was gained.

There were many others who attempted dependence proofs and failed, like Proclus, so that, by the beginning of the seventeenth century, the problem was still an unsolved and highly controversial one.

The first real progress in settling the question of the independence of the parallel axiom was made by Saccheri (1667–1733), an Italian Jesuit priest and a professor of mathematics at the University of Pavia. He conceived the brilliant idea of denying Euclid's parallel axiom, hoping thereby to deduce contradictory theorems and thus establish the truth of the axiom.

For his investigations, Saccheri chose the birectangular, isosceles quadrilateral $ABCD$, with angles A and B right angles and sides AD and BC equal.*   Then, on the basis of Euclid's parallel axiom, angles C and D are right angles; therefore Saccheri first assumed that these angles C and D were obtuse.   He then proved that Euclid's parallel axiom was a consequence of this assumption.   But from the parallel axiom it then followed that these angles were right angles, and a contradiction had been reached.

Saccheri next assumed that angles C and D were acute, hoping to arrive again at a contradiction.   But it never appeared, despite the proof of one theorem after another.   Had he realized that these theorems represented a perfectly logical, consistent geometry different from Euclid's, Saccheri would have anticipated the discovery of non-Euclidean geometry by at least a hundred years.   Instead, his works went almost completely unnoticed until Beltrami, the distinguished Italian mathematician, convinced the scientific world of their worth.

The next investigations of note were those of the German mathematician J. H. Lambert (1728–1777).   He took as his fundamental figure the quadrilateral with three right angles and examined the hypotheses in which the remaining angle was in turn right, obtuse, and acute.   His results, like those of Saccheri, were indefinite and unsatisfactory.   The investigations continued, however.

12.3. The Founders of Non-Euclidean Geometry

It finally dawned on mathematicians of the late eighteenth and early nineteenth centuries that the unending record of failure in the search for a proof of the parallel axiom was not due to any lack of ingenuity on the part of mathematicians but, rather, to the fact that the parallel postulate was independent of the others.   This means that it is possible to replace the parallel axiom by a different one and, on the new axiomatic basis, to develop a logical system different from Euclid's.

The three mathematicians who finally broke with tradition and developed a geometry in which Euclid's parallel axiom was denied were Gauss (1777–1855) of Germany, Bolyai (1802–1860) of Hungary, and Lobachevski (1793–1856) of Russia.   Bolyai's discovery, made in 1823, at the age of twenty-one, was not published until 1832; Lobachevski's was published in 1829; while Gauss, uncertain of his results and fearing the loss of prestige, failed to publish his results.

* For an illustration of this figure see Fig. 14.10.

Although Gauss, Bolyai, and Lobachevski apparently worked independently of each other and in different parts of the world, each of them conceived the idea of replacing Euclid's parallel axiom by the new axiom that, *through a point not on a line, there is more than one parallel to the line.* The resulting geometry is the classic non-Euclidean system called hyperbolic geometry. It corresponds to the geometry originating from Saccheri's acute-angle hypothesis.

Unlike Bolyai, Lobachevski was a prolific writer, inspired, perhaps, by his great desire to gain world-wide recognition for his geometry. Unfortunately, recognition failed to come during his lifetime, but as if to atone for her neglect, the world often refers to hyperbolic geometry as Lobachevskian geometry.

Once hyperbolic geometry had been developed and accredited, other non-Euclidean geometries appeared. Chief among them was elliptic geometry, first developed by Riemann (1826–1866) of Hanover, Germany, and described in his inaugural address, delivered in 1851, upon his admission as an unpaid instructor to the University of Göttingen.

In rejecting not only the parallel postulate but also the postulate that a straight line was infinite, Riemann broke with Euclidean geometry even more drastically than did his predecessors. He assumed that every line was endless and finite in length. His resulting geometry is that suggested by Saccheri's obtuse-angle hypothesis.

The possibility of a second kind of elliptic geometry was seen and developed later by Felix Klein (1849–1925) of Germany. His geometry and Riemann's are usually distinguished by designating Klein's as elliptic, and Riemann's as spherical, geometry. Some writers however, prefer the respective names single elliptic, and double elliptic, geometry.

12.4. Non-Euclidean Geometry and the Calculus

The second period in the development of non-Euclidean geometry was characterized chiefly by investigations from the standpoint of the calculus and differential geometry, in which properties of surfaces are studied. These investigations were inspired by more practical scientists who had found Riemann's geometry rich in helpful facts, but also in generalities which needed refinement for dealing with infinitely small quantities.

In the calculus approach to geometry, a study is made of the expression

$$ds^2 = \frac{dx_1{}^2 + dx_2{}^2 + dx_3{}^2}{1 + (K/4)(x_1{}^2 + x_2{}^2 + x_3{}^2)}$$

for arc length between two points (x_1, x_2, x_3) and $(x_1 + dx_1,\ x_2 + dx_2,\ x_3 + dx_3)$ of a space. The constant K is the curvature of the space.

According as K is greater than, equal to, or less than zero, the space has constant positive curvature, zero curvature, or constant negative curvature.

For $K = 0$, this expression reduces to

$$ds^2 = dx_1{}^2 + dx_2{}^2 + dx_3{}^2$$

which will be recognized as the square of the differential of arc length in Euclidean space. (By properly defining angle, area, and volume in terms of this differential of arc length, ds, it is possible to develop all the theorems of Euclidean geometry and thus eliminate the axiomatic approach to this familiar system.)

Prominent among the investigators of this period was the great physicist Helmholtz (1821–1894), who discussed, among other things, the relation between the forms just given for arc length and the assumption of free mobility, "Spatial magnitudes can be moved from one place to another without distortion."

Later the Norwegian mathematician S. Lie (1842–1899) linked Helmholtz's investigations with group theory and showed that there are three types of groups which characterize the three geometries: Euclidean, hyperbolic, and elliptic.

Even these brief remarks will show that the developments of this period go beyond the confines of elementary mathematics. They are mentioned here chiefly to indicate other approaches to non-Euclidean geometry.

12.5. Consistency and Independence Proofs

The second period in the development of non-Euclidean geometry is also noteworthy for the many consistency proofs which appeared. The question of the consistency of a logical system has long been a troublesome, difficult, and challenging one. In the development of any logical system, there is always the burden of proving that the system is consistent by showing that no contradictions can occur. No contradiction has ever been found in either hyperbolic or elliptic geometry, but this fact does not constitute proof that they are consistent.

Usually the consistency of a geometry is established by giving meaning to its undefined elements in terms of elements of Euclidean geometry. Then, axioms and theorems of the new system will correspond to theorems of this latter geometry and hence be as consistent as it is. However, a satisfactory proof of the consistency of Euclidean geometry has never been given. Customary proofs usually refer the question to concepts of coordinate geometry and hence ultimately to the number concept, whose consistency is still an open question.

In 1868, Beltrami (1835–1900), a professor at Bologna, showed how hyperbolic geometry could be represented with suitable restrictions on a Euclidean surface of constant Gaussian curvature. He showed thereby that this geometry was as consistent as Euclid's.

Many other proofs have appeared since Beltrami's, but, like his, they are for the most part analytical in character and attain their goal by showing that the analytical representations lead to sets of consistent equations.

As already pointed out in Sec. 2.5, the questions of consistency of a geometry and of the independence of its axioms are related ones. Consistency proofs have therefore brought to a triumphant close those many and magnificent efforts to prove the independence of Euclid's parallel axiom.

12.6. Later Developments

The third period in the development of non-Euclidean geometry is associated with the investigations of men such as Cayley, Klein, Clifford, and others, who deserted the classical axiomatic approach to this system and substituted for it the metric approach. Because of its vital importance in the unifying of geometric theory, this metric approach is discussed in more detail in the following paragraphs of this chapter.

EXERCISES

1. State the assumptions that Euclid, Lobachevski, and Riemann each made regarding (a) the number of parallels to a line; (b) the extent of a line.

2. Describe Saccheri's method of proving Euclid's parallel axiom.

3. Has Euclidean geometry been proved to be consistent? Hyperbolic geometry? Elliptic geometry? Explain.

4. Has proof been given that Euclid's parallel axiom is independent of his other axioms? Give reasons for your answer.

THE PROJECTIVE METRIC APPROACH

12.7. Projective Definition of Distance; of Angle

Up to this point, the discussion of non-Euclidean geometry has centered around Euclid's parallel axiom and modifications of this axiom. The projective metric approach, which is more elegant, begins with extremely sophisticated definitions for distance and angle in the projective plane. These Cayley-Klein definitions are stated first and then discussed.

An arbitrary conic of the plane, called the *absolute*, is chosen. Assume for the present that this conic is nondegenerate. Then, any line in the plane not a tangent to the conic meets it in two distinct points, say O and U, and the distance AB between the given points A and B is, by definition, any one of the values

$$AB = c \log (OU,AB)^* \tag{1}$$

where c is an arbitrary constant and (OU,AB) is the cross ratio of the four points O, U, A, B (Fig. 12.1).

Dually, any two lines a, b (Fig. 12.2) meet in a point P, and from P there are two tangents o and u to the absolute

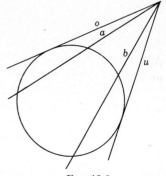

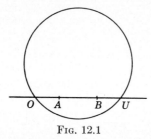

FIG. 12.1   FIG. 12.2

conic. The angle (ab) between the lines is by definition any one of the values:

$$\angle ab = c' \log (ab,ou)$$

where c' is an arbitrary constant.

For the present, no consideration is given the special cases which arise when the points and lines in question are on the conic or are tangent to the conic.

There is not space here for a full and complete motivation of these definitions, but a few preliminary remarks will emphasize some of their significant features. Certainly the many concepts appearing in the definitions, such as an *absolute conic*, a *cross ratio*, a *logarithm*, and an *arbitrary constant*, are confusing, but justifications can be given for all of them. The cross-ratio and logarithm concepts are discussed first.

Just as in elementary geometry distance and angle are invariants of rigid motion, so too in projective geometry it is desired to have distance and angle invariant under projective transformations. It is also desired that formulas for these quantities have Euclidean formulas as special cases.

* In the complex plane, the logarithmic function has period $2n\pi$.

Although cross ratio has the desired invariance property, it involves four elements, not two, and so two additional points O, U were paired with the points A and B in order to define the projective distance AB. The points O and U are the intersections of line AB with the arbitrarily chosen conic (Fig. 12.1). Thus, distance in projective geometry is not an inherent property of two points, but a property of these points in relation to a certain arbitrarily chosen conic.

Furthermore, if A, B, C are three collinear points in the Euclidean plane, the distances AB, BC, AC satisfy the additive relation

$$AB + BC = AC$$

and it is desired to have this property satisfied by the new definition of distance.

But, the cross ratios (OU,AB), (OU,BC), (OU,AC) do not satisfy the additive relation, since

$$(OU,AB) + (OU,BC) \neq (OU,AC) \tag{2}$$

They do, however, satisfy the relation

$$(OU,AB) \cdot (OU,BC) = (OU,AC)*$$

and, by a well-known theorem of logarithms,

$$\log (OU,AB) + \log (OU,BC) = \log (OU,AC) + 2n\pi$$

Hence, apart from the ambiguity due to the periodicity of the log function, the log of a cross ratio, rather than the cross ratio itself, has the desired additive property.

The role of the absolute conic and the arbitrary constant which enters into the new definition will be brought out in the illustrations of the next two sections.

12.8. Projective Distance Illustrated

The projective distance AB between two points A, B of the projective plane will be calculated when the absolute is the special conic given by the equation

$$x_1{}^2 + x_2{}^2 - x_3{}^2 = 0$$

and the two points $A\,(0,0,1)$, $B(x,0,1)$, $-1 < x < 1$, are on the line

$$x_2 = 0$$

[In the Euclidean plane, this conic is a circle of unit radius having points $O(-1)$ and $U(1)$ as extremities of a diameter (Fig. 12.3).]

* In this connection see Exercise 2 following Sec. 10.8.

Since a set of nonhomogeneous coordinates, or parameters, for the collinear points O, A, B, U are, respectively, -1, 0, x, 1, the cross ratio (OU,AB) is, by formula (2), Sec. 10.7,

$$(OU,AB) = \frac{1 - x}{1 + x}$$

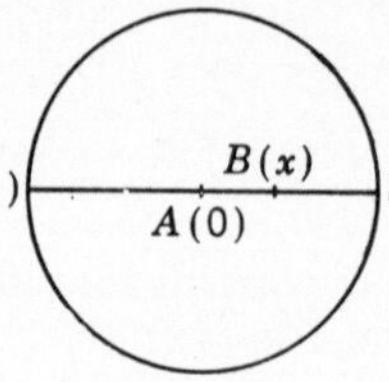

FIG. 12.3

and the projective distance AB is then

$$AB = c \log \frac{1 - x}{1 + x}$$

When B is at A, $x = 0$, and hence $AA = 0$. Thus, the new distance from point A to itself is zero, as is desired.

But, when B is at U, an unexpected result occurs. By the usual limit processes, as $B \rightarrow U$, $x \rightarrow 1$, $\log [(1 - x)/(1 + x)] \rightarrow -\infty$, and by Sec. 10.9

$$AU = -\infty$$

Similarly, as $B \rightarrow O$, $x \rightarrow -1$, $\log [(1 - x)/(1 + x)] \rightarrow \infty$, and

$$AO = \infty$$

Thus a very surprising result has been obtained: *The projective distance from the center A of a circle to either extremity of the diameter through A is infinite.* (In the Euclidean plane the line segment AO had unit length.)

12.9. Projective Angle Illustrated

The projective definition of angle is illustrated when the absolute conic is the degenerate conic

$$x_3{}^2 = 0$$

If two given lines a, b intersect at point P, the tangents from P to this degenerate conic are the lines denoted P_I and P_J, joining P to the circular points at infinity, and the projective angle ϕ between the lines is given by the expression

$$\phi = c' \log (P_I P_J, ab) \tag{1}$$

where c' is an arbitrary constant.

If now P is taken as the origin of a rectangular coordinate system and if the slope m of a line through the two points (x_1, y_1), (x_2, y_2) is a quantity given by the formula

$$m = \frac{y_2 - y_1}{x_2 - x_1}$$

then the slopes of the lines P_I, P_J are, respectively, i and $-i$

$$(i = \sqrt{-1})$$

Therefore if m_1, m_2 are the respective slopes of lines a, b, the cross ratio $(P_I P_J, ab)$, for convenience denoted r, is given by the expression

$$r = (P_I P_J, ab) = \frac{(m_1 + i)(m_2 - i)}{(m_1 - i)(m_2 + i)} \tag{2}$$

and the Euclidean angle θ between the lines a, b is given by the formula

$$\tan \theta = \frac{m_1 - m_2}{1 + m_1 m_2} \tag{3}$$

or, using (2) and (3),

$$\tan \theta = \frac{1}{i}\left(\frac{r-1}{r+1}\right) \tag{4}$$

which, when compared with the well-known relation

$$\tan \theta = \frac{1}{i}\left(\frac{e^{2\theta i} - 1}{e^{2\theta i} + 1}\right) \tag{5}$$

gives $r = e^{2\theta i}$, and hence

$$\theta = \frac{1}{2i} \log (P_I P_J, ab) \tag{6}$$

Thus, for $c' = 1/2i$, the formulas for projective angle and Euclidean angle are alike.

Furthermore, when

$$(P_I P_J, ab) = -1$$
$$\log (P_I P_J, ab) = \pi i$$

and from (6)

$$\theta = \frac{1}{2i}\pi i = \frac{\pi}{2}$$

The lines a, b are then *perpendicular*.

12.10. A New Definition of Parallel Lines

Since metric projective geometry is primarily concerned with the real points of the plane, a distinction will be made now between the cases when the absolute conic is real and when it is nonreal.

The equation

$$k(x_1{}^2 + x_2{}^2) + x_3{}^2 = 0$$

where k is any real number, represents a real conic if $k < 0$, a degenerate conic if $k = 0$, and an imaginary conic if $k > 0$. Hence, if a line meets the conic in the points O, U, these infinitely distant points are:

Distinct and real if $k < 0$ and the conic is real.

Coincident and real if $k = 0$ and the conic is degenerate.

Conjugate imaginary if $k > 0$ and the conic is imaginary.

A new definition of parallel lines now enters the discussion: *If parallel lines are defined as lines meeting at an infinitely distant (ideal) point of the line*, there will be *two, one, or no* parallels to a line L of the projective plane through a point P not on L according as the absolute conic is *real, degenerate,* or *imaginary.*

12.11. Hyperbolic, Parabolic, and Elliptic Metric Geometries

It is at this precise point that projective metric geometry automatically subdivides into three different systems. The geometry which results when there are two infinitely distant (ideal) points on a line, and consequently a right- and a left-handed parallel to a line, is the classical Bolyai-Lobachevski system called *hyperbolic* geometry; the second metric system, which results when there is only one infinitely distant point on a line, and hence only one parallel to the line, is *parabolic* geometry, the system which so beautifully extends and generalizes Euclid; and the third metric system, which results when there is no infinitely distant (ideal) point on a line, and hence no parallel to the line, is *elliptic* geometry, the system first developed by Riemann.

(The names hyperbolic, parabolic, and elliptic were proposed by Felix Klein in two monographs appearing in the years 1871 and 1873. The names were suggested to him by the fact that the existence of two real, two imaginary, or two coincident parallels corresponds precisely to the behavior of the asymptotes to the hyperbola, the ellipse, and the parabola.)

The relation between these various geometries has been exhibited by means of the character of the points in which a line met the absolute conic. Since any projective transformation which leaves the absolute unaltered will not disturb the character of metric theorems, the new geometries may also be defined as a study of properties of figures invariant under those projective transformations that leave the associated absolute conic invariant. This is the earlier definition given in Sec. 11.12.

Concluding Remarks

One final remark is made in closing this chapter. Although non-Euclidean geometries were developed originally as exercises in logic, they were later found to be of inestimable value to the scientists who were dealing with changing quantities, with spaces of more than three dimensions, and with other situations which had no parallel in the more or less static Euclidean theory.   Non-Euclidean geometry dovetailed beautifully with many of their new theories, and thus a new mathematical background accompanies experiments of the atomic age. Mathematics is continually enriching the world with some of her finest gifts.

EXERCISES

1. Are conclusions of non-Euclidean geometry true?   Valid?   Explain.

2. What can be said about the consistency of non-Euclidean geometry?

3. Why is the log of a cross ratio used in the projective definition of distance?

4. In which non-Euclidean geometry is the projective distance from a point of the plane to an ideal point a real number?   A nonreal number?

5. How many parallels to a line are there in parabolic geometry?

Chapter 13

PARABOLIC GEOMETRY

Parabolic geometry is the metric projective geometry in which the absolute is the degenerate conic

$$x_3{}^2 = 0$$

Points (x_1, x_2, x_3) of the projective plane for which $x_3 = 0$ have already been labeled ideal points, and hence every point of the line $x_3 = 0$ is ideal. Conversely, all ideal points of the plane satisfy the equation $x_3 = 0$ and hence lie on this line. This special line $x_3 = 0$ is called, therefore, *the ideal line of the plane;* all other lines are ordinary lines.

Since an ordinary line of the parabolic plane meets the absolute conic (now the ideal line of the plane) in a single point, and since two lines which meet on the absolute are parallel, *there is in parabolic geometry one and only one parallel to a line through a point not on it.*

Also, in this geometry, it is possible to show [26, pp. 116–123] that the algebraic expressions for projective distance and angle are identical with formulas (1) and (2) of Sec. 11.1 for distance and angle in the Euclidean plane.

Furthermore, when the nonhomogeneous coordinate x of a point P of an ordinary line L is taken to be its distance from a fixed point O of the line, the infinitely distant point $P(\infty)$ of L is its ideal point, and all parallels to L meet at $P(\infty)$.

These preliminaries would seem to suggest that parabolic geometry *is* Euclidean geometry, but it must be remembered that the two systems are based on different definitions and different axiomatic structures.

Thus, in parabolic geometry, two lines always *intersect, even when they are parallel,* whereas in Euclidean geometry, two parallel lines *never meet,* however far they are produced. It is this failure of parallel lines to meet which is constantly hampering geometric reasoning in the elementary science, so that tiresome enumeration of exceptional cases is required.   One such occurs in the case of points that are harmonic in accordance with the definition of Sec. 4.1.   The four points A, B, C, D of Fig. 4.1 were harmonic when C and D were points in which the interior and exterior bisectors of angle P of the triangle APB met the base AB.   An exception occurs here when P is the vertex of the isosceles triangle PAB (Fig. 13.1), for the interior bisector of angle P then meets the base at its mid-point C (Why?), and the exterior bisector, being parallel to the base, does not meet it.   There is then no point D on AB extended such that $AC/CB = -AD/DB$, and hence *the mid-point C of the base has no harmonic conjugate in the Euclidean plane.*

One way to avoid such exceptional cases is to assume that, on each Euclidean line, there is one and only one infinitely distant point, the point where all parallels to the line meet it.   But, such an assumption is confusing to the beginner, who reasons thus: How can parallel lines, which never meet, meet at an infinitely distant point?

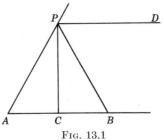

FIG. 13.1

It seems well to avoid either confusion or an extended discussion of the logic of this situation by simply showing in what sense parabolic geometry extends and generalizes Euclid. This is done in what follows.

13.1. The Cross Ratio of a Harmonic Set of Points

In the purely projective definition (Sec. 8.1) of harmonic points, two of the points A, B were diagonal points of a quadrangle, while the remaining points C, D were points in which the remaining sides of the quadrangle met the line AB.

Although no mention was made in this definition of the lengths of line segments, it is still possible to show that the cross ratio (AB,CD) of these points has the numerical value -1.   The proof will make use only of the invariance of cross ratio on projection.

Let the lines QS and RP of Fig. 8.1 meet at a point O.   Then the harmonic points A, B, C, D project through R into the points S, Q, O, D.   These points, in turn, project through point P into the points B, A, C, D.   If then x denotes the value of the cross ratio (AB,CD),

$$x = (AB,CD) = (SQ,OD) \qquad \text{(by projection from } R\text{)}$$
and $\quad x = (SQ,OD) = (BA,CD) \qquad \text{(by projection from } P\text{)}$

But, since changing the order of the elements in one pair changes the value of the cross ratio to its reciprocal,

$$(BA,CD) = \frac{1}{(AB,CD)}$$

and hence

$$x = \frac{1}{x} \qquad x^2 = 1 \qquad \text{and} \qquad x = \pm 1$$

Since harmonic points separate each other,

$$x = -1$$

and proof has been given of the following theorem:

Theorem 13.1

   The cross ratio (AB,CD) of the points A, B, C, D, harmonic in accordance with definition of Sec. 8.1, has the numerical value -1.

13.2. The Harmonic Conjugate of the Ideal Point of a Line

   The harmonic conjugate of an ideal point of a line may now be defined. If A, B are two distinct, ordinary points of the parabolic plane, *the harmonic conjugate of the ideal point $D(\infty)$ of line AB is by definition the mid-point C of the line segment AB.*

   An immediate consequence of this new definition and Theorem 13.1 is:

Theorem 13.2

   The ideal point $D(\infty)$ of a line AB divides the line segment AB into the ratio -1.

   It is shown in elementary coordinate geometry of the Euclidean plane that any point $P(x)$ of the line joining the distinct points $A(a)$, $B(b)$ divides the directed line segment AB into the ratio r, where, *if r is any real number not equal to -1,*

$$x = \frac{a + rb}{1 + r}$$

There is no point in this plane corresponding to $r = -1$, but in parabolic geometry the point corresponding to $r = -1$ is, by virtue of Theorem 13.2, the ideal point of the line, and the exceptional case of the Euclidean plane has been removed.

   Another consequence of the new definition is noted. The interior and exterior bisectors PC and PD of angle P of triangle PAB (Fig. 13.1) are harmonic conjugates of the lines PA, PB. Thus, perpendicular lines in the Euclidean plane have become harmonic conjugates in the parabolic plane.

Also, since PD meets line AB at the ideal, or infinitely distant, point $D(\infty)$ and since this point divides the line segment AB into the ratio -1, another parabolic theorem is:

Theorem 13.3

> *The exterior bisector of an angle of a triangle meets the base at a point dividing the opposite side into segments proportional to the adjacent sides.*

The exceptional case of this theorem which occurred in the Euclidean plane when the triangle PAB was isosceles was illustrated in Fig. 13.1. No exception occurs in the parabolic plane, owing to the presence of the ideal point $D(\infty)$ on line AB.

13.3. Construction of a Parallel with Straightedge Only

Another remarkable consequence of the definition of the last section is that only a straightedge is needed to construct a line parallel to a given line if the mid-point of any segment of the line is given.

The construction, if M is the mid-point of the line segment AB, is as follows: Draw any two lines through point A and let a line through M meet these lines in the points P and R (Fig. 13.2). If line BP meets AR in S and line BR meets AP in Q, line SQ is the required parallel. (Why?)

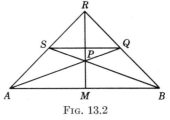

FIG. 13.2

A reversal of this construction *locates with straightedge alone the mid-point of a line segment when any parallel to the line is given.*

These constructions should be compared with corresponding ones in elementary geometry, where use is made of both straightedge *and compasses* (see Exercises 3, Sec. 13.4).

13.4. Another Elementary Construction with Straightedge Only

Another elementary construction, using only the straightedge, is to divide a line segment into n equal parts when only a parallel to the segment is given. Successive repetitions of the above construction will effect this result when n is a power of 2. (Why?)

The construction is made now when n is a number k, not a power of 2, such as $k = 5$.

Divide any segment B_0M parallel to AB (Fig. 13.3) into eight equal parts by the points B_0, B_1, . . . , B_5, . . . , B_8. (Eight is the first power of 2 greater than the given value $k = 5$.)

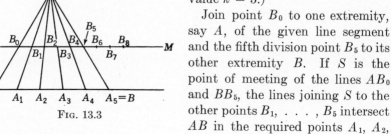

Fig. 13.3

Join point B_0 to one extremity, say A, of the given line segment and the fifth division point B_5 to its other extremity B. If S is the point of meeting of the lines AB_0 and BB_5, the lines joining S to the other points B_1, . . . , B_5 intersect AB in the required points A_1, A_2, A_3, A_4, $(A_5 = B)$. The extension to any value of k not a power of 2 is obvious.

EXERCISES

1. How many parallels to a line through a point not on the line are there in parabolic geometry?

2. What does the absolute conic become in parabolic geometry?

3. Compare the construction of a parallel in Sec. 13.3 with an elementary one using compasses and straightedge. Could the construction of Sec. 13.3 have been used in the Euclidean plane? Why?

13.5. Ideal Points Used to Prove Cross-ratio Theorems

Let the four collinear points A, B, C, D (Fig. 13.4) be projected from a point O into the points A', B', C', D' on a line through C parallel to OD. Then $C = C'$; D' is the ideal point of the line; and by Theorem 13.2

$$\frac{A'D'}{D'B'} = -1$$

But

$$(A'B',C'D') = \frac{A'C'}{A'D'} \bigg/ \frac{C'B'}{D'B'}$$

and hence

$$(A'B',C'D') = -\frac{A'C'}{C'B'} = \frac{A'C'}{B'C'}$$

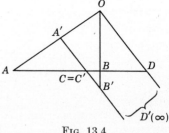

Fig. 13.4

Because of the invariance of cross ratio on projection,

$$(AB,CD) = (A'B',C'D') = \frac{A'C}{B'C} = \lambda$$

and thus a single ratio rather than a double ratio appears in the cross-ratio formula when D' is *the ideal point* of the line $A'B'$. This fact greatly simplifies the proofs of Theorems 4.10 to 4.12. Thus

$$(CD,AB) = (BA,DC) = (DC,AB) = A'C/B'C = \lambda$$

and Theorem 4.10 is proved. Also, reversal of the order in one pair changes the cross ratio to its reciprocal, for

$$(AB,DC) = \frac{B'C}{A'C} = \frac{1}{\lambda} = (BA,CD) = (CD,BA) = (DC,AB)$$

and Theorem 4.11 is proved.

To prove Theorem 4.12, it is noted first that

$$(AC,BD) = \frac{A'B'}{CB'} = \frac{A'C + CB'}{CB'} = 1 - \lambda$$

and
$$(AD,BC) = \frac{A'B'}{A'C'} = \frac{A'C' + C'B'}{A'C'} = 1 - \frac{1}{\lambda}$$

$$= \frac{\lambda - 1}{\lambda}$$

Therefore, from Theorem 4.11,

$$(AD,CB) = \frac{\lambda}{\lambda - 1}$$

and Theorem 4.12 is proved.

13.6. The Quadrilateral with Two Ideal Points as Vertices

Special interest is attached to the quadrilateral in which two vertices, say A, B, are ideal points (Fig. 13.5). If P, Q, R, S are its remaining vertices, lines RS and PQ are parallel, and so are the lines PS and RQ. The quadrilateral is therefore the familiar parallelogram of the elementary curriculum.

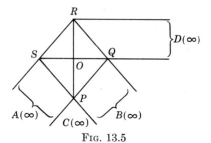

Fig. 13.5

Since the line AB is the ideal line of the plane, the diagonals PR and QS meet AB at the respective ideal points $C(\infty)$ and $D(\infty)$; and since both the sets of points R, O, P, C and S, O, Q, D are harmonic, the mid-point of the diagonal SQ lies on the mid-point of the diagonal RP. Thus proof has been given of the following elementary theorem:

Theorem 13.4

The diagonals of a parallelogram bisect each other.

EXERCISE

Prove the parabolic theorem: A line bisecting two sides of a triangle is parallel to the third side and equal to half of it.

13.7. A Generalization of an Elementary Theorem

Ceva's theorem was used earlier to prove the theorem that the medians of a triangle are concurrent. It is now possible to show that this theorem is only a special case of a much more general theorem of projective geometry. The new theorem is:

Theorem 13.5

> *If three distinct points, one on each side of a triangle, are collinear, the three lines which join their harmonic conjugates with respect to the vertices of the triangle to the opposite vertices are concurrent.*

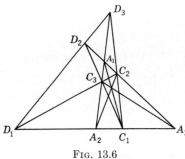

FIG. 13.6

PROOF. Let A_1, A_2, A_3 (Fig. 13.6) be vertices of the given triangle and let side a_i be opposite the vertex A_i, $i = 1, 2, 3$. Also, let D_1, D_2, D_3 be the three collinear points such that D_i is on side a_i and C_i is the conjugate of point D_i. Then, the theorem will be proved by showing that triangle $C_1C_2C_3$ is perspective to triangle $A_1A_2A_3$. This will necessitate showing that the sides C_3C_2, C_3C_1, C_1C_2 of triangle $C_1C_2C_3$ pass through the respective points D_1, D_2, D_3.

To show, for example that side C_2C_3 passes through point D_1, project side A_1A_2 from point D_1 on the line A_1A_3. Then points A_1, A_2, and D_3 project into the respective points A_1, A_3, and D_2; and since C_3 is the fourth harmonic point to A_1, A_2, and D_3, C_3 must project into the fourth harmonic point C_2 to A_1, A_3, and D_2. Consequently C_2C_3 passes through D_1. Similarly, side C_1C_3 passes through D_2 and side C_1C_2 through D_3. The triangles $A_1A_2A_3$ and $C_1C_2C_3$ are, therefore, perspective, and hence the lines A_1C_1, A_2C_2, A_3C_3 joining corresponding vertices are concurrent. Thus the theorem is proved.

When line $D_1D_2D_3$ is the ideal line of the plane, point C_i is the midpoint of side a_i, and Theorem 13.5 reduces to the familiar theorem: *The medians of a triangle are concurrent.*

13.8. The Classification of Conics

Projective (nonmetric) definitions for conics were given in Sec. 9.9, and point and line equations were obtained for them in Sec. 10.15, but no attempt was made in either case to classify the resulting conics. This will be done now for conics in the parabolic plane, and again ideal points will figure prominently in the classification.

A conic is first defined to be a *hyperbola*, a *parabola*, or an *ellipse* according as it contains *two* distinct ideal points (Fig. 13.7*a*), *one* ideal point (Fig. 13.7*b*), or *no* real ideal point (Fig. 13.7*c*).

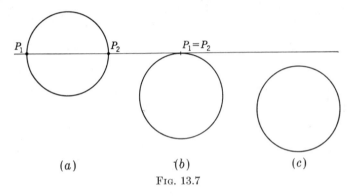

$$(a) \qquad\qquad (b) \qquad\qquad (c)$$

FIG. 13.7

When the general equation of a conic in homogeneous coordinates is

$$A x_1^2 + B x_1 x_2 + C x_2^2 + D x_1 x_3 + E x_2 x_3 + F x_3^2 = 0 \qquad (1)$$

the conic will meet the ideal line

$$x_3 = 0$$

in ideal points $(x_1, x_2, 0)$ satisfying the equation

$$A x_1^2 + B x_1 x_2 + C x_2^2 = 0 \qquad (2)$$

From the theory of quadratic equations, (2) will have two distinct, real roots, one real root, or no real root according as

$$B^2 - 4AC \gtreqless 0$$

Hence the conic contains two, one, or zero ideal points according as $B^2 - 4AC \gtreqless 0$, and this statement combined with the definition just given leads to the familiar test:

According as $B^2 - 4AC$ is greater than, equal to, or less than zero, the conic (1) is, respectively, a hyperbola, a parabola, or an ellipse.

EXERCISES

1. Classify the following conics:

(a) $x_1{}^2 + 4x_1x_2 + x_2{}^2 + x_1x_3 = 0$

(b) $x_1{}^2 - 4x_1x_2 + x_3{}^2 = 0$

(c) $3x_1{}^2 + 3x_2{}^2 - 6x_1x_3 = 0$

2. State and prove the dual of Theorem 13.5.

3. Is the dual of Theorem 13.5 the same as its converse?   Give reasons for your answer.

Chapter 14

HYPERBOLIC GEOMETRY

The early axiomatic approach and the later metric approach to hyperbolic geometry given in Chap. 12 stressed only the new parallel theory and not its strange consequences. Some of these will be illustrated now by means of models.

As explained in Chap. 2, a model of an abstract system is any set of elements satisfying its axioms. Once such a set has been found, familiar properties of these elements may be translated into theorems of the abstract system, and in this way the rather tedious axiomatic method of developing a science is avoided. Besides, a model at the start often suggests queer, unfamiliar theorems and lends an air of reality to some of the almost incredible new findings which would have been difficult, if not impossible, to anticipate by logical reasoning alone.

Fortunately, there are two famous models for the new geometry, one due to Klein, the other to Poincaré. Klein's model, which is described first, will be used primarily for illustrating the new parallel theory and for a discussion of the consistency of the new system. Before this is done, however, a few words will be said about the classical axiomatic approach to the new science, and a first basic theorem will be proved by the familiar deductive reasoning process.

14.1. The Classical Axiomatic Approach

An axiomatic basis for hyperbolic geometry is sets 1 to 4 and set 6 of Hilbert's axioms, Appendix B, together with the following replacement for Axiom 5, Appendix B:

Axiom 5'

> *Through a given point not on a given line, more than one line can be drawn not meeting the given line.*

The new axiom is not so unnatural as it might seem. Suppose that a ray through a point P not on a line L rotates about P, first in the counterclockwise direction until it meets a parallel ray PA, and then in the clockwise direction until it meets a second parallel ray PA' (Fig. 14.1). Why should it be assumed, as is done in Euclidean geometry, that the rays PA and PA' coincide in the same line, the unique parallel PM to L? It is just as reasonable to assume that these lines are distinct, as shown in Fig. 14.1.

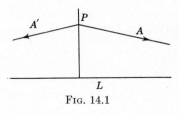

FIG. 14.1

Suppose that this latter assumption is made. How will the resulting theory differ from Euclid's? A first answer to this question is as follows: Theorems which do not depend on the new parallel theory or new definitions—in particular, the first 28 theorems of Euclid, Book I (see Sec. 4, Appendix A)—are available for immediate use in hyperbolic geometry. However, our present discussion is chiefly concerned not with common theory but rather with new and different results, and the first of these differences concerns the number of parallels to a line L through a point P not on L. By parallels are here meant lines which do not meet L.

Suppose that two distinct lines L' and L'' through a point P not on line L *do not meet* L (Fig. 14.2). Then, if O is the foot of the perpendicular from P to L, one pair of vertical angles formed by the lines L' and L'' contains the line PO. Any line PX in the other (shaded) pair of vertical angles formed by these lines does not meet L, for if PX

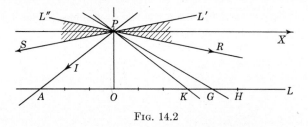

FIG. 14.2

met L at a point M, then by Pasch's axiom (Axiom 2.4, Appendix B) the line L'', through the vertex P of the triangle POM, would meet L. But L'' was, by hypothesis, a nonintersecting line, and a contradiction has been reached.

Since PX was any line through P lying in the shaded vertical angles, it then follows that *there are an infinite number of lines through point P not meeting line L.*

Of this infinite set of nonintersecting lines, two particular ones will now be singled out for attention, and called parallel lines.

As the line PO rotates about O in the counterclockwise direction, it intersects line L for a time and then ceases to intersect L. Consequently, lines through point P are divided into the two sets: S_1, containing only intersecting lines, and S_2, containing only nonintersecting lines. From the continuity axioms, set 6, Appendix B, it then follows that *there is a line dividing one of these sets from the other.*

To which set does the dividing line belong? To answer this question, it is observed first that the dividing line of the two sets must be either the last line of set S_1 or the first line of set S_2. But, there is no last line in set S_1, for if there were, it would meet L in a point G. Then, there would be a point H on L at a finite distance from O and on the opposite side of G from O. The line PH would then be an intersecting line, and PG would not be the last line of set S_1. This means that the dividing line of the two sets is a first line of set S_2. Call it PR. Similarly, another dividing line is encountered as PO rotates in the clockwise direction. Call it PS.

These two special nonintersecting lines, PR and PS, are called the respective *left- and right-handed parallels to L through point P.*

It will be shown next that the angles RPO and SPO which these parallels make with PO are equal.

Suppose that one of these angles, say SPO, is greater than the other. Then, there is a line PI forming with PO an angle α equal to angle RPO. Let PI intersect line L at a point A. Then take a point K on the opposite side of O from A so that

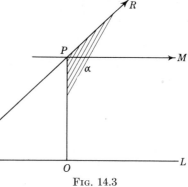

FIG. 14.3

$$OK = AO$$

Draw PK. Since the right triangles OPA and OPK are congruent, corresponding angles OPA and OPK are equal, and hence PK coincides with PR. But PK intersects L, and PR does not intersect L. From this contradiction follows the equality of the angles RPO and SPO.

It is shown next that these angles are acute.

If $\angle RPO = \angle SPO = \alpha$ equals 90°, lines PR and PS coincide in the perpendicular through P to PO (Fig. 14.3), and there is then only one parallel to L through P, contrary to the hypothesis.

If $\alpha > 90°$, then all lines lying in the shaded angle OPR (Fig. 14.3) are intersecting lines. But one of them is the perpendicular through point P to line L.   It does not meet L (Why?), and again a contradiction has been reached.   Thus proof has been given of the basic theorem:

Theorem 14.1

> *If P is any point not on a line L, there are two distinct lines PR and PS which do not intersect L, and they form equal acute angles with the perpendicular PO to L.   Any line through P in the domain bounded by PR and PS and not containing the perpendicular PO is a nonintersecting line.   All other lines through P intersect L.*

Starting with this basic new theorem, it is now possible to deduce one hyperbolic theorem after another and in this way to arrive at a body of conclusions representing the new geometry.   The process, which is omitted here, may be found treated in detail in the literature [74].

EXERCISES

1. Show that the following are valid theorems in hyperbolic geometry:
(*a*) Two triangles are congruent if two sides and the included angle, two angles and the included side, or three sides of one triangle are equal to the corresponding parts of the other.
(*b*) In an isosceles triangle, the angles opposite the equal sides are equal.
2. Without using the parallel axiom, prove that an exterior angle of a triangle is greater than either of the interior and opposite angles.   *Hint:* See [74, p. 8].
3. Prove the hyperbolic theorem: The sum of two angles of a triangle is less than 180°.

14.2. Klein's Model

Klein's model for the real hyperbolic plane is constructed by taking some familiar elements of elementary geometry and renaming them in such a way that all but one of Euclid's axioms are satisfied.   The one exception is the famous parallel axiom.

In the model, the (real) hyperbolic plane consists of points interior to a given circle C (Fig. 14.4).   Ordinary points of the plane are distinguished from these interior points by calling the latter H-points. Chords of the circle are then taken as models of lines and are distinguished from ordinary lines by calling them H-lines.   All points outside the circle are ignored.

Since two points within the circle determine a chord and since two chords intersect in one and only one point, two H-points determine an H-line and two H-lines intersect in an H-point.   Thus Hilbert's incidence axioms (Sec. 2, Appendix B) are satisfied by elements of the model.

Distance in the model is given by the definition (1) of Sec. 12.7 for $c = 1$. Thus, if the H-line AB (Fig. 14.5) meets circle C in points O and U, the distance (AB) between the H-points A and B is

$$(AB) = \log (OU,AB)$$

By the arguments of Sec. 12.8, O and U are then the infinitely distant, or ideal, points of the line AB; all ideal points lie on the circumference of circle C; and the line is an open continuum of points on which Euclidean order and continuity axioms (Secs. 3 and 6, Appendix B) hold.

Congruency axioms are a trifle more difficult to verify, but it can be done. Furthermore, if X is an H-point not on the H-line AB, the

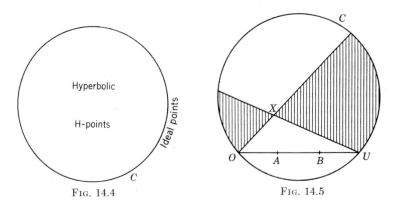

FIG. 14.4   FIG. 14.5

lines XO and XU are models of the respective left- and right-handed parallels to this line.

Actually seeing a model of two parallels to a line forces the reader to discard some old-fashioned ideas about how parallels should look. The H-lines XU and XO of Fig. 14.5 are parallels, not because of their appearance in a drawing, but because of the new definition of parallel lines, given in Sec. 12.10.

14.3. Concerning Independence and Consistency Questions

Klein's model is satisfactory for illustrating the new theory of parallels but not for visualizing many of the new theorems. However, it has served a far more useful purpose. Throughout the Middle Ages and up to the beginning of the nineteenth century, all efforts to prove the dependence of Euclid's parallel axiom on his other axioms had failed. Klein's model showed the inherent impossibility of such a proof. If the parallel axiom could be deduced from Euclid's other axioms, it would be a theorem in the geometry of Klein's model, and proof has just been given that it is not.

Mathematical genius of a rare order went in to the finding of the model. Once it had been found, hyperbolic geometry was seen to be as consistent as Euclid's, since if a theorem and its contradiction could both be deduced in the new science, the same would be true in Euclidean geometry.

EXERCISES

1. Why are the first 28 theorems of Euclid, Book I, valid theorems of hyperbolic geometry?

2. Does a (hyperbolic) line through point X (Fig. 14.5), lying within the shaded region, intersect (hyperbolic) line AB? Give reasons for your answer.

3. Prove that, if one line of the hyperbolic plane is parallel to a second, the second is parallel to the first. *Hint:* See [74, p. 69.]

4. Is the following Euclidean theorem valid in hyperbolic geometry: "An exterior angle of a triangle is greater than either opposite interior angle."? Give reasons for your answer.

14.4. Stereographic Projection and Poincaré's Model

Because Poincaré's model for hyperbolic geometry will be obtained by a stereographic projection, some elementary facts about such a projection are given first.

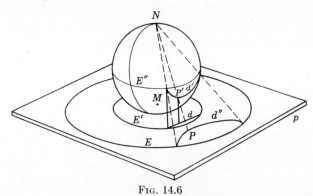

FIG. 14.6

Suppose a sphere tangent at M to a horizontal plane p is projected from its highest point N on the plane (Fig. 14.6). Then, to each point P' of the sphere corresponds the point P in which line NP' meets plane p. The single exception occurs when point P' is N. This map of the sphere $P \rightarrow P'$ is called a stereographic projection, and two properties of such a projection are:

Property 1

Circles on the sphere not through N are mapped into circles of the plane, and conversely every circle in the plane is the image of a circle on the sphere.

Property 2

Stereographic projection reproduces angles on the sphere without distortion.

Proofs, which are omitted, may be found in the literature [31, pp. 248–254].

Poincaré's model will now be described. The hyberbolic plane is first represented by the interior of circle E' lying in the horizontal plane p of Fig. 14.6. A sphere of the same radius r as E' is tangent to this plane at the center M of E'. The circumference and interior of E' are projected by a vertical parallel projection on the lower half of the sphere and its boundary circle E''. Then, each chord d of circle E' projects into a semicircle d' orthogonal to circle E''. If interior points of E' are points of Klein's model, the semicircle d' is the image of an H-line of the latter.

Now, map the lower hemisphere, whose boundary is E'', back on the horizontal plane by a stereographic projection from the point N (Fig. 14.6). By property 1, circle E'' maps into the circle E of the plane p, and each point of the hemisphere is mapped into an interior point of this circle. Because of the angle-preserving and circle-preserving nature of stereographic projection, semicircles d' of the hemisphere are mapped into circular arcs d'' orthogonal to circle E, and thus to each chord (H-line) of circle E' corresponds an arc orthogonal to circle E. Instead of studying the geometry of Klein's model, one may therefore study the geometry of points and orthogonal arcs of the fixed circle E. They constitute Poincaré's model of points and lines of the hyperbolic plane.

Since there is a 1-1 correspondence between the set of all circular arcs orthogonal to circle E and the set of chords of circle E', *two interior points of circle E determine one and only one arc orthogonal to circle E.**

Also, it follows from Exercise 5, Sec. 5.4, that, when two orthogonal circles intersect in two distinct points and are each orthogonal to a third circle, the two circles have one point of intersection inside, and the other outside, the circle. Hence, two orthogonal arcs intersect in one and only one point of circle E. Incidence axioms are therefore

* See also Exercise 6 following Sec. 5.4.

satisfied by points and orthogonal arcs (lines) of circle E, and every Euclidean theorem dealing with the incidence of points and lines has its analogue in the model.

The distance AB between two points A and B of the model is given by the definition:

> *If the orthogonal arc joining points A and B of circle E meets the circle in points O and U (Fig. 14.7), the distance AB is*
>
> $$AB = \log{(OU,AB)} = \log\left(\frac{OA/AU}{OB/BU}\right)$$
>
> *where OA, AU, OB, BU are chords of the orthogonal arc AB.*

By the same arguments as those given in Sec. 12.8, the distance from a point of arc AB to either O or U is infinite, and orthogonal arcs

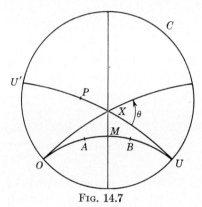

FIG. 14.7

XO and XU through a point X not on AB are models of the respective right- and left-handed parallels to the line AB (Fig. 14.7).

One beauty of Poincaré's model is its conformal nature. That is, the angle between orthogonal arcs is the angle between two hyperbolic lines, as given by the Cayley-Klein definition of Sec. 12.7. (Proof of this fact is left for more advanced investigations.)

The fact that the angle between two hyperbolic lines is the angle between tangents to the corresponding orthogonal arcs of Poincaré's model at their point of intersection, is used now in illustrating some hyperbolic theorems that directly contradict Euclid.

14.5. Concerning the Sum of the Angles of a Triangle

To illustrate the theorem concerning the sum of the angles of a triangle of the hyperbolic plane, let ABC be the figure formed by arcs

AC, CB, BA, each orthogonal to a fixed circle with center E (Fig. 14.8). Because this figure is a model of a hyperbolic triangle, it is called the triangle ABC, even though its sides are curved. Inversion theory will be used to show that the sum of its angles is less than $180°$.

Let the orthogonal arcs AC and BC of Fig. 14.8 meet at a second point R. Invert the entire figure with R as a center of inversion and let the inverse of a point, say A, be denoted A'.

By Theorem 5.4, arcs AC and BC invert into the intersecting lines $A'C'$ and $B'C'$ of Fig. 14.9; and by Theorem 5.5, the fixed circle (E) inverts into a circle orthogonal to lines $A'C'$ and $B'C'$ and hence into a circle with center at C'.

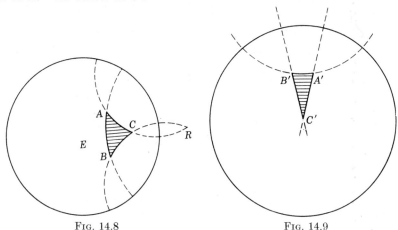

FIG. 14.8   FIG. 14.9

Since the circular arc AB inverts into the circular arc $A'B'$ orthogonal to circle (C'), its center is outside this circle. But the triangle $A'B'C'$ of Fig. 14.9, formed by two straight lines and this orthogonal arc, has an angle sum less than the triangle whose vertices are A', B', C' and whose sides are all straight lines. Since the latter triangle has its angle sum equal to $180°$, the triangular figure $A'B'C'$ bounded by two straight lines and a curved line has an angle sum less than $180°$. But, by Theorem 5.7, angles are unchanged on inversion, and hence the same is true of the original triangle ABC. Thus proof has been given of the hyperbolic theorem:

Theorem 14.2

The sum of the angles of a triangle is less than $180°$.

Other proofs of this theorem may be found in the literature [74, p. 81; 31, pp. 256–258].

Since a quadrilateral (Fig. 14.10) consists of the two triangles ABC and ADC, whose angle sum equals the sum of the angles of the quadrilateral, a second hyperbolic theorem is:

Theorem 14.3

The sum of the angles of a quadrilateral is less than 360°.

14.6. The Saccheri and Lambert Quadrilaterals

Distance is used in describing the Saccheri quadrilateral $ABCD$ of Fig. 14.10. This figure is a quadrilateral whose angles at A and B are right angles and whose sides BC and AD are of *equal length*. *Angles C and D are then called the summit angles of the quadrilateral,* and a theorem concerning such a quadrilateral is:

Theorem 14.4

The summit angles of a Saccheri quadrilateral are equal and acute.

The theorem is illustrated in Fig. 14.10 and proved easily on the basis of the congruency theorems and Theorem 14.2 [74, pp. 77–79].

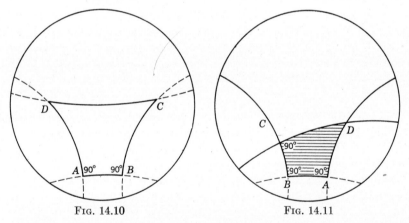

FIG. 14.10   FIG. 14.11

The historic Lambert quadrilateral also has a queer property. Since three of its angles A, B, C are right angles (Fig. 14.11), its fourth angle D is, by virtue of Theorem 14.3, *acute.* Consequently, an incredible hyperbolic theorem is:

Theorem 14.5

There are no squares in hyperbolic geometry.

Similar triangles also have lost a familiar property in the new science. If two similar triangles, such as ABC and $A'B'C'$ (Fig. 14.12), have

their corresponding angles A and A', B and B', C and C' equal, and
if these two triangles are not congruent, then the quadrilateral $BB'C'C$
has an angle sum of 360°, contrary to Theorem 14.3. Hence another
unfamiliar theorem is:

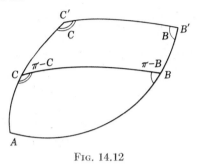

FIG. 14.12

Theorem 14.6

Two similar triangles are congruent.

14.7. The Angle of Parallelism. Absolute Units

It was shown in Sec. 14.1 that the parallels XU and XO to line AB
(Fig. 14.7) make equal angles with the perpendicular XM to AB.
Also, if a denotes the length of the line segment XM, it is shown in
more detailed investigations dealing with the trigonometry of the
hyperbolic plane [74, pp. 148–150] that

$$\tanh a = \cos \alpha$$

where the angle α is *the angle of parallelism for the distance* a, and
another hyperbolic theorem stated without proof is:

Theorem 14.7

*The angle of parallelism for any given distance is a constant. As the
angle increases, the distance decreases.*

Because of the 1-1 correspondence which exists between a distance a
and the angle α of parallelism, and because a line segment may be
constructed when its angle of parallelism is given, the unit of length in
hyperbolic geometry is called an absolute unit. That is, the unit
can be determined without reference to some arbitrary standard, in
contrast to a unit like the meter, which is the distance between two
marks on a certain bar of platinum preserved by the French government, or the English yard, which is the distance between two marks
on a metal bar kept by the English government, or the pound, which

represents the quantity of matter contained in a metallic cylinder kept at the U.S. Bureau of Standards.   Such units are called *relative* units.

Since the length of any segment in hyperbolic geometry may be designated by referring to its associated angle of parallelism and since angles may be constructed with great precision without reference to any bureau of standards, the unit of length in hyperbolic geometry does not vary as the years go by.

14.8. Other Facts

There are other theorems which, because of the new distance concept, are not so well illustrated in Poincaré's model.   For example, if the parallel XU to line AB (Fig. 14.7) meets the fixed circle at the second point U', it is possible to show that, as a point P of line XU approaches U, the distance from P to line AB *decreases*, and as P approaches U', this distance *increases*.   A point P on line XU between X and U is said to lie in the *direction of parallelism*, and the queer property of parallel lines just mentioned is described in more formal language in the theorem:

Theorem 14.8

> *Two parallel lines converge continuously in the direction of parallelism and diverge continuously in the opposite direction.*

Area theorems too are quite different in the new system.   For example, if x is the sum of the angles of a triangle, $180 - x$ is its defect, and one theorem dealing with area is:

Theorem 14.9

> *The areas of two triangles are proportional to their defects.*

As the defect approaches zero, the area of a triangle also approaches zero; therefore a hyperbolic triangle of sufficiently small area will have a defect which is small and an angle sum close to 180°, i.e., a sum close to the sum of the angles of a Euclidean triangle.

14.9. Another Model.   The Pseudosphere

It is customary to illustrate many of the strange properties of hyperbolic figures by means of figures on the pseudosphere (Fig. 14.13), a surface formed by revolving a curve called the tractrix about an asymptote.   Positions taken by the tractrix, while it is being rotated, such as BC and AD of the figure, are called meridians of the surface.   They are models of hyperbolic lines.   Since these models are curved lines, it is to be expected that figures formed by them will have lost many familiar properties of figures in the Euclidean plane. On the pseudo-sphere, for example, parallel lines are seen to approach each other in the direction of parallelism, as stated in Theorem 14.8; two triangles have different angle sums, as implied in Theorem 14.9; and even a Saccheri quadrilateral $ADCB$ with its two acute summit angles no longer seems like the figment of a wild imagination.

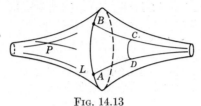

FIG. 14.13

Unfortunately, a study of this model takes one out of the realm of elementary mathematics and hence must be reserved for more advanced investigations.

EXERCISES

1 Prove that in a Lambert quadrilateral (see Sec. 14.6) the sides adjacent to the acute angle are greater than their respective opposite sides.

2. Which is greater, the base or the summit of a Saccheri quadrilateral? Prove your answer.

3. Prove that the segment joining the mid-points of two sides of a triangle is less than one-half the third side.

4. Prove that two Saccheri quadrilaterals with equal summits and equal summit angles, or with equal bases and equal summit angles, are congruent.

14.10. Hyperbolic Geometry and the Physical Universe

Originally, hyperbolic geometry represented a very excellent exercise in logic, but once man had freed himself of outmoded beliefs, his imagination soared to the point where he actually conceived the idea of applying the new science to the physical universe.

Lobachevski, observing that Euclidean trigonometric formulas are valid in the infinitesimally small neighborhood of a point of the hyperbolic plane, considered the possibility of his geometry replacing Euclid's in astronomical space. A crucial experiment, he thought, would consist in finding a positive lower bound for the parallax of stars. His experiment was doomed to failure, since such a lower bound, if it exists, is smaller than the allowance for experimental error. Failure of the experiment would merely mean that, if space is hyperbolic, the absolute unit must be many million times as large as the diameter of the earth's orbit.

It is not difficult, however, to imagine a universe subject to hyperbolic laws. Suppose, for example, that, in a huge sphere of astronomically large radius r, the temperature T changes from point to point in accordance with the law

$$T = c(r^2 - h^2)$$

where c is a constant and h is the distance of a point P from the center O of the sphere. The temperature T then has a maximum value for h equal to zero, is equal to zero for h equal to r, and is constant on any concentric sphere.

Under the assumption that people and objects in this fanciful world are so susceptible to the heat that they grow large or small with the temperature, it is possible to show that the shortest distance path joining two points within the sphere is along an arc of a circle orthogonal to the sphere. Thus, if a plane through the center of the sphere intersects the sphere in the circle C, the shortest distance curve joining two points A, B within C is along the arc orthogonal to C. Also, if this arc meets C in the points O and U (Fig. 14.7) arc AB is the shortest distance path for a person, say P, walking along this path to the boundary point U of his world. As P walks toward U, his distance from the center of the sphere increases, and hence his body shrinks and his steps become shorter. P would therefore get the distinct impression that he would never reach the boundary, no matter how many steps he would take. Nor would measuring instruments help him, for all objects are assumed to contract as their distance from the center increases. The observer's world would therefore seem to be infinite in extent.

If now the earth is placed in this sphere, so that an observer at point X is very near the center of the sphere, the shortest distance paths through X are circular arcs XO and XU orthogonal to C. Furthermore, if the radius of the sphere is sufficiently large, these arcs would look like straight lines, and the angle θ between these arcs would then be so small that no instrument would be fine enough to detect a value for it other than zero. The parallels XO and XU would then seem to coincide in a single line, and the observer would doubtless conclude that through the point X there is one and only one parallel to the line AB, as in Euclidean geometry. The inadequacy of visual observation or of measurements for determining the character of space is obvious.

Chapter 15

ELLIPTIC GEOMETRY

An investigation is to be made now of elliptic geometry, in which the absolute conic is imaginary and *there is no parallel to a line.*

The distance between two real points of the elliptic plane will be real only if the arbitrary constant c in the definition of Sec. 12.7 is taken to be a real number. When this is done, the real elliptic line is closed, finite in length, and contains only ordinary points.

Since great circles on a sphere are closed curves, all of which have the same finite length, the sphere immediately presents itself as a model for elliptic geometry, with its points and great circles being identified with points and lines of the abstract system. However, the fact that these great circles always intersect in two distinct points and not in one point, as do lines in the projective plane, is a disturbing factor. Also, since there are infinitely many great circles through two diametrically opposite points of the sphere, two points do not always determine one and only one line; therefore incidence axioms of projective geometry are not satisfied by these great circles.

It was Klein who first saw how to rid Riemann's original elliptic geometry of this one blemish—if it may be called a blemish—and his investigations led to a second type of geometry in which there is no parallel to a line. The basic difference between Klein's and Riemann's geometries is explained first.

15.1. Elliptic and Spherical Geometry

It is assumed in what follows that the reader is familiar with elementary properties of figures on a sphere. For instance, in Fig. 15.1 great circles through the points A and B of the sphere are perpendicular to the great-circle arc AB joining these points, and the two great circles meet at two points N and S, called the *poles* of this arc AB. Riemann assumed that these poles were distinct: Klein, that they coincided.

The geometry in which a line has two distinct poles is called *spherical* geometry and that in which a line has one and only one pole is called *elliptic* geometry.   (Some writers prefer the respective names double and single elliptic geometry.)

The elliptic plane in Riemann's geometry has the character of a

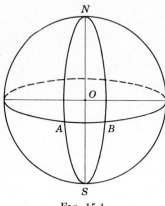

two-sided surface such as a sphere, on which the two sides are usually distinguished by calling one the inside and the other the outside.   In Klein's geometry, the plane has the character of a one-sided surface, a simple example of which is the Möbius leaf.   This surface is described in the next section.

Fig. 15.1

15.2. The Möbius Leaf

Take a long, narrow rectangular strip of paper $ABCD$ (Fig. 15.2) and form a surface by joining the opposite sides AB and CD after first rotating one of them, say CD, about its mid-point through an angle of 180°.   Corners C and D will then coincide (Fig. 15.3) with corners A and B, respec-

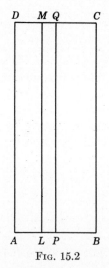

Fig. 15.2

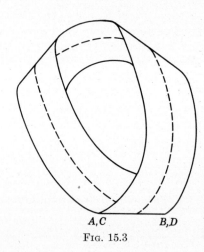

Fig. 15.3

tively, and the two sides of the surface will become indistinguishable. In other words, the surface has one side.

One way of distinguishing a one-sided surface from a two-sided one is to fix a point on the surface and a direction of rotation about it.

If a point describes a closed path upon a two-sided surface, then when the point has returned to its initial position, the final direction of rotation coincides with the initial one. On a one-sided surface, however, there exist closed paths for which the original and final directions of rotation are opposite. This can be seen by drawing a line PQ in the middle of the rectangle $ABCD$ and noting the path on the resulting Möbius surface. A bug crawling along the line PQ will return to its original position upside down. To see why, take a pencil with an eraser at its top and let the pencil describe the path PQ. If at the start the pencil is in the position NP (Fig. 15.4), then at the end, the eraser will be at point N' of the same figure such that $\angle NPN' = 180°$. Thus N and N' are on opposite sides of P.

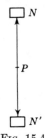

Fig. 15.4

A painter who contracts to paint a Möbius strip will find when he has returned to his starting line, that he has done twice as much work as he had intended to do. Your model will explain why.

EXERCISES

1. If O (Fig. 15.5) is the pole of the great-circle arc AB of a sphere, and if OA is extended to a point O' so that $O'A = OA$, (a) what theorems of Euclidean

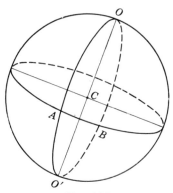

Fig. 15.5

geometry are needed to prove that O', B, and O are collinear? (b) Do these theorems depend on either the parallel axiom or the infinite extent of a line? (c) Prove that $O'B$ is perpendicular to AB and equal to OB, where $O'B$, OB, and AB are great-circle arcs of the sphere.

2. Name a theorem of Euclidean geometry which does not depend on either the parallel axiom or the infinite extent of the line. Is it a theorem of elliptic geometry? Why?

3. If A and B are two points of a sphere, how many great circles are there through these two points? Give reasons for your answer.

4. (*a*) Cut the Möbius leaf along the line PQ (Fig. 15.2). Into how many parts does the cut divide the surface?   (*b*) If the cut is made along the line LM (Fig. 15.2), where rectangle $ALMD$ is one-third of the rectangle $ABCD$, interpret the results on the Möbius leaf.

5. How many edges has the Möbius leaf?   Give reasons for your answer.

15.3. Models

Now that a distinction has been made between spherical and elliptic geometry, models will be given for each.

A model for elliptic geometry is obtained by taking only half the sphere, a hemisphere with its boundary circle C, and identifying its points and great-circle arcs with points and lines of the plane.

Since elliptic lines are closed, each point A of circle C must be identified with its diametrically opposite point A' so that a great-circle arc with extremities at A and A' (Fig. 15.6) represents a closed line.

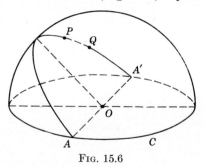

Fig. 15.6

In construction problems, all points which lie on arcs extending beyond the boundary of the hemisphere are to be replaced by their diametrically opposite points.

The metric of the model is that of the sphere itself with the understanding that, if PQ denotes any segment of a line, it is known which of the two segments determined by P and Q is meant.   Thus, in Fig. 15.6 segment PQ could be the dotted segment or the heavy segment containing the point A, which is now identified with its diametrically opposite point A'.

The angle θ between two lines of the elliptic plane is taken to be the angle between corresponding arcs representing these lines, and the angle is always understood to be less than 180°.   This agreement is necessary in order that two sides and an included angle will determine one and only one triangle on the surface.

Since, as shown in Sec. 10.1, points and great-circle arcs of the hemisphere may be put into 1-1 correspondence with points and lines of the projective plane, the latter may be taken as a model of elliptic geometry, and all theorems dealing with the incidence of points and lines, such as Desargues' theorem, are valid in the elliptic plane.

A model for spherical geometry may be taken to be the sphere itself. In contrast to the situation in elliptic geometry, the line in spherical geometry now has two poles, and the axiom that two lines intersect in a point is replaced by the following theorem:

Theorem 15.1

Two lines intersect in two points and enclose an area.

This theorem is illustrated in Fig. 15.5, where the great-circle arcs OAO' and OBO' enclose a portion of the surface of the sphere.

A number of theorems of elliptic geometry will be illustrated in what follows.

15.4. Basic Theorems of Elliptic Geometry

The great-circle arcs NA and NB of Fig. 15.1 are models of perpendicular lines in the elliptic plane and illustrate the following theorem:

Theorem 15.2

Two perpendiculars to a line meet in a point.

The proof of the theorem follows immediately from the axiom that two lines of the plane always meet.

For visualizing some of the following theorems, it will be convenient to think of the earth's surface as a perfect sphere. Its meridians are then models of lines perpendicular to the equator, and since these meridians all meet at the north and south poles, there is illustrated the next theorem (15.3) of elliptic (or spherical) geometry.

Theorem 15.3

The perpendiculars at all points of a line are concurrent in a point called the pole of the line, and conversely every line through the pole is perpendicular to the line.

The distance q from a pole of a line to the line is, by definition, the polar distance to the line, and a theorem concerning polar distance is:

Theorem 15.4

In any triangle ABC in which angle C equals $90°$, angle A is less than, equal to, or greater than $90°$ according as the segment BC is less than, equal to, or greater than the polar distance q.

The theorem is illustrated in Fig. 15.7, where $\angle B = \angle C = 90°$, angle $A < 90°$, and $BC < q$. Then $\angle A + \angle B + \angle C > 180°$, and the same figure also illustrates the next theorem:

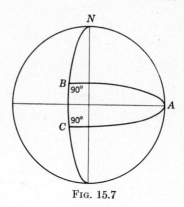

FIG. 15.7

Theorem 15.5

The sum of the angles of a triangle is greater than 180°.

An immediate consequence of this theorem is:

Theorem 15.6

The sum of the angles of a quadrilateral is greater than 360°.

Because the angle sum of a triangle differs in parabolic, hyperbolic, and elliptic geometry, the angle sum theorem is often used to classify these various systems. Thus, *according as the angle sum of a triangle is greater than, equal to, or less than* 180°, *the geometry is, respectively, elliptic, parabolic (Euclidean), or hyperbolic.*

EXERCISES

1. Draw figures illustrating each of the following elliptic theorems and prove them:

(*a*) In an isosceles triangle, the sides opposite equal angles may be unequal.

(*b*) The sum of two sides of a triangle may be less than the third side.

2. Why is Euclid's Theorem 16, Appendix A, not necessarily true in elliptic geometry? *Hint:* See [11, p. 130].

15.5. The Saccheri and Lambert Quadrilaterals

Saccheri's historical birectangular isosceles quadrilateral $ABCD$ with right angles at A and B and equal sides AD and BC is illustrated in Fig. 15.8. As in hyperbolic geometry, the summit angles C and D

are equal, and, by virtue of Theorem 15.6, these same angles are obtuse.   Thus another theorem of elliptic geometry is:

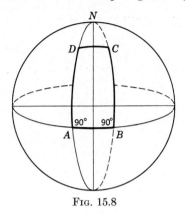

Fig. 15.8

Theorem 15.7

   The summit angles of a Saccheri quadrilateral are equal and obtuse.

   Proofs of the following three theorems are left as exercises:

Theorem 15.8

   In a Lambert quadrilateral ABCD in which

$$\angle A = \angle B = \angle C = 90°$$

   the fourth angle D is obtuse.

Theorem 15.9

   There are no squares in elliptic geometry.

Theorem 15.10

   Two similar triangles are congruent.

EXERCISE

   Which is greater, the base or the summit of the Saccheri quadrilateral in the elliptic plane?   Prove your answer.

15.6. Area Theorems

   Strange facts about areas are illustrated in Fig. 15.9, where each of the triangles ABC, $A'B'C'$, and $A'B''C''$ is equiangular and equilateral. The respective sides AB, $A'B'$, and $A'B''$ have lengths:

$$AB < q \qquad A'B' = q \qquad A'B'' > q$$

where q is the polar distance.   It then follows from Theorem 15.4 that in these triangles

$$\angle BAC < 90° \qquad \angle B'A'C' = 90° \qquad \angle B''A'C'' > 90°$$

If by the excess of a triangle is meant the quantity $x - 180$ where x is its angle sum, the excesses e_1, e_2, e_3 of the successive triangles

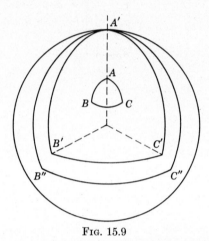

Fig. 15.9

ABC, $A'B'C'$, $A'B''C''$ are positive (Why?) and satisfy the relations

$$e_1 < 90° \qquad e_2 = 90° \qquad e_3 > 90°$$

A closer examination of Fig. 15.9 shows that the triangle $A'B''C''$ of largest excess has the largest area and makes more plausible the following theorem:

Theorem 15.11

The area of a triangle is proportional to its excess.

15.7. Elliptic Geometry and the Physical Universe

The possibility of using elliptic theorems to describe laws of the universe was explored by Gauss, who thought that he would settle once and for all the question of which one of the metric geometries— hyperbolic, parabolic, or elliptic—best described the physical universe.

Since the theorem concerning the angle sum of a triangle differed in the three geometries, Gauss decided to measure the angles of a large triangle.   He needed a large triangle, since the angle sums of a triangle in all three geometries were known to be in close agreement for small regions, but would differ radically in astronomically large domains. Gauss therefore stationed an observer on each of three fairly distant mountain peaks, with instructions to each observer to measure the angle formed by light rays from his point of observation to each of the remaining observers.

When the data were collected, it was found that the angle sum was within 2 seconds of 180°, and so nothing was settled. Allowance had to be made for errors of measurement, for the fact that the triangle might not have been sufficiently large, and for the possibility that the light rays which formed the sides of his triangle were curved. However, the experiment, although inconclusive, did bring out the significant fact that all three geometries are in close agreement for sufficiently small regions, a situation closely paralleling that in physics, where the systems of Newton and Einstein are in close agreement for small distances and velocities, but differ widely for astronomically large quantities.

Other experiments have been made, e.g., terrestial experiments on two rays of light perpendicular to one plane. Results seem to indicate that these lines remain equidistant as expected in Euclidean geometry, but it is quite conceivable that in a sufficiently large domain they might diverge, as expected in hyperbolic geometry, or converge, as expected in elliptic geometry. Furthermore, conclusions based on measuring instruments which are in turn based on one or the other of these different geometries would hardly be convincing.

However, it can be said in conclusion that elliptic geometry has demonstrated its usefulness in the Einstein theory of relativity, in optics, and in the general theory of wave propagation. The revolutionary importance of non-Euclidean geometry, including both hyperbolic and elliptic geometry, lies in the overthrow of the erroneous belief that Euclidean geometry was the only possible mathematical description of the physical universe.

SUGGESTIONS FOR FURTHER READING

(Chapters 12 to 15)

Bonola, R.: "Non-Euclidean Geometry."
Carslaw, H. S.: "The Elements of Non-Euclidean Geometry."
Cooley, H. R., D. Gans, M. Kline, and H. Wahlert: "Introduction to Mathematics," Chap. 22.
Courant, R., and H. Robbins: "What Is Mathematics?", pp. 214–227.
Coxeter, H. S. M.: "Non-Euclidean Geometry."
Hilbert, D., and S. Cohn-Vossen: "Geometry and the Imagination."

Klien, Felix: "Elementary Geometry from an Advanced Standpoint," pp. 174–188.
Kline, Morris: "Mathematics in Western Culture," Chap. 26.
Lieber, Hugh G., and Lillian R. Lieber: "Non-Euclidean Geometry."
Manning, Henry P.: "Non-Euclidean Geometry."
Wolfe, H. E.: "Introduction to Non-Euclidean Geometry."
Young, J. W.: "Lectures on Fundamental Concepts of Algebra and Geometry," pp. 14–35.
Young, J. W. A.: "Monographs on Modern Mathematics," pp. 93–151.

Appendix A

EARLY FOUNDATION OF EUCLIDEAN GEOMETRY*

1. The Definitions of Book I

1. A point is that which has no part.
2. A line is breadthless length.
3. The extremities of a line are points.
4. A straight line is a line which lies evenly with the points on itself.
5. A surface is that which has length and breadth only.
6. The extremities of a surface are lines.
7. A plane surface is a surface which lies evenly with the straight lines on itself.
8. A plane angle is the inclination to one another of two lines in a plane which meet one another and do not lie in a straight line.
9. And when the lines containing the angle are straight, the angle is called rectilineal.
10. When a straight line set up on a straight line makes the adjacent angles equal to one another, each of the equal angles is right, and the straight line standing on the other is called perpendicular to that on which it stands.
11. An obtuse angle is an angle greater than a right angle.
12. An acute angle is an angle less than a right angle.
13. A boundary is that which is an extremity of anything.
14. A figure is that which is contained by any boundary or boundaries.
15. A circle is a plane figure contained by one line such that all the straight lines falling upon it from one point among those lying within the figure are equal to one another.
16. And the point is called the centre of the circle.
17. A diameter of the circle is any straight line drawn through the center and terminated in both directions by the circumference of the circle, and such a straight line also bisects the circle.
18. A semicircle is the figure contained by the diameter and the circumference cut off by it. And the centre of the semicircle is the same as that of the circle.
19. Rectilineal figures are those which are contained by straight lines, trilateral

* Sections 1 to 4 are taken from "The Thirteen Books of Euclid's Elements," 2d ed., a translation from the text of Heiberg with introduction and commentary by Thomas L. Heath. Used by permission of The Macmillan Company for Cambridge University Press, London, 1926.

figures being those contained by three, quadrilateral those contained by four, and multilateral those contained by more than four straight lines.

20. Of trilateral figures, an equilateral triangle is that which has its three sides equal, an isosceles triangle that which has two of its sides alone equal, and a scalene triangle that which has its three sides unequal.

21. Further, of trilateral figures, a right-angled triangle is that which has a right angle, an obtuse-angled triangle that which has an obtuse angle, and an acute-angled triangle that which has its three angles acute.

22. Of quadrilateral figures, a square is that which is both equilateral and right-angled; an oblong that which is right-angled but not equilateral; a rhombus that which is equilateral but not right-angled; and a rhomboid that which has its opposite sides and angles equal to one another but is neither equilateral nor right-angled. And let quadrilaterals other than these be called trapezia.

23. Parallel straight lines are straight lines which, being in the same plane and being produced indefinitely in both directions, do not meet one another in either direction.

2. The Postulates

Let the following be postulated:
1. To draw a straight line from any point to any point.
2. To produce a finite straight line continuously in a straight line.
3. To describe a circle with any centre and distance.
4. That all right angles are equal to one another.
5. That, if a straight line falling on two straight lines makes the interior angles on the same side less than two right angles, the two straight lines, if produced indefinitely, meet on that side on which are the angles less than the two right angles.

3. The Common Notions

1. Things which are equal to the same thing are also equal to one another.
2. If equals be added to equals, the wholes are equal.
3. If equals be subtracted from equals, the remainders are equal.
4. Things which coincide with one another are equal to one another.
5. The whole is greater than the part.

4. The Forty-eight Theorems of Book I

1. On a given finite straight line, to construct an equilateral triangle.
2. To place at a given point (as an extremity) a straight line equal to a given straight line.
3. Given two unequal straight lines, to cut off from the greater a straight line equal to the less.
4. If two triangles have the two sides equal to two sides, respectively, and have the angles contained by the equal straight lines equal, they will also have the base equal to the base, the triangle will be equal to the triangle, and the remaining angles will be equal to the remaining angles, respectively, namely, those which the equal sides subtend.
5. In isosceles triangles the angles at the base are equal to one another, and, if the equal straight lines be produced further, the angles under the base will be equal to one another.
6. If in a triangle two angles be equal to one another, the sides which subtend the equal angles will also be equal to one another.

7. Given two straight lines constructed on a straight line (from its extremities) and meeting in a point, there cannot be constructed on the same straight line (from its extremities), and on the same side of it, two other straight lines meeting in another point and equal to the former two, respectively, namely, each to that which has the same extremity with it.

8. If two triangles have the two sides equal to two sides, respectively, and have also the base equal to the base, they will also have the angles equal which are contained by the equal straight lines.

9. To bisect a given rectilineal angle.

10. To bisect a given finite straight line.

11. To draw a straight line at right angles to a given straight line from a given point on it.

12. To a given infinite straight line, from a given point which is not on it, to draw a perpendicular straight line.

13. If a straight line set up on a straight line make angles, it will make either two right angles or angles equal to two right angles.

14. If with any straight line, and at a point on it, two straight lines not lying on the same side make the adjacent angles equal to two right angles, the two straight lines will be in a straight line with one another.

15. If two straight lines cut one another, they make the vertical angles equal to one another.

16. In any triangle if one of the sides be produced, the exterior angle is greater than either of the interior and opposite angles.

17. In any triangle two angles taken together in any manner are less than two right angles.

18. In any triangle the greater side subtends the greater angle.

19. In any triangle the greater angle is subtended by the greater side.

20. In any triangle two sides taken together in any manner are greater then the remaining one.

21. If on one of the sides of a triangle, from its extremities, there be constructed two straight lines meeting within the triangle, the straight lines so constructed will be less than the remaining two sides of the triangle, but will contain a greater angle.

22. Out of three straight lines, which are equal to three given straight lines, to construct a triangle: thus it is necessary that two of the straight lines taken together in any manner should be greater than the remaining one.

23. On a given straight line and at a point on it, to construct a rectilineal angle equal to a given rectilineal angle.

24. If two triangles have the two sides equal to two sides, respectively, but have the one of the angles contained by the equal straight lines greater then the other, they will also have the base greater than the base.

25. If two triangles have the two sides equal to two sides, respectively, but have the base greater than the base, they will also have the one of the angles contained by the equal straight lines greater then the other.

26. If two triangles have the two angles equal to two angles, respectively, and one side equal to one side, namely, either the side adjoining the equal angles, or that subtending one of the equal angles, they will also have the remaining sides equal to the remaining sides and the remaining angle to the remaining angle.

27. If a straight line falling on two straight lines make the alternate angles equal to one another, the straight lines will be parallel to one another.

28. If a straight line falling on two straight lines make the exterior angle equal

202 APPENDIX A

to the interior and opposite angle on the same side, or the interior angles on the same side equal to two right angles, the straight lines will be parallel to one another.

29. A straight line falling on parallel straight lines makes the alternate angles equal to one another, the exterior angle equal to the interior and opposite angle, and the interior angles on the same side equal to two right angles.

30. Straight lines parallel to the same straight line are also parallel to one another.

31. Through a given point to draw a straight line parallel to a given straight line.

32. In any triangle, if one of the sides be produced, the exterior angle is equal to the two interior and opposite angles, and the three interior angles of the triangle are equal to two right angles.

33. The straight lines joining equal and parallel straight lines (at the extremities which are) in the same directions (respectively), are themselves also equal and parallel.

34. In parallelogrammic areas the opposite sides and angles are equal to one another, and the diameter bisects the areas.

35. Parallelograms which are on the same base and in the same parallels are equal to one another.

36. Parallelograms which are on equal bases and in the same parallels are equal to one another.

37. Triangles which are on the same base and in the same parallels are equal to one another.

38. Triangles which are on equal bases and in the same parallels are equal to one another.

39. Equal triangles which are on the same base and on the same side are also in the same parallels.

40. Equal triangles which are on equal bases and on the same side are also in the same parallels.

41. If a parallelogram have the same base with a triangle and be in the same parallels, the parallelogram is double of the triangle.

42. To construct, in a given rectilineal angle, a parallelogram equal to a given triangle.

43. In any parallelogram the complements of the parallelograms about the diameter are equal to one another.

44. To a given straight line, to apply, in a given rectilineal angle, a parallelogram equal to a given triangle.

45. To construct, in a given rectilineal angle, a parallelogram equal to a given rectilineal figure.

46. On a given straight line, to describe a square.

47. In right-angled triangles the square on the side subtending the right angle is equal to the squares on the sides containing the right angle.

48. If in a triangle the square on one of the sides be equal to the squares on the remaining two sides of the triangle, the angle contained by the remaining two sides of the triangle is right.

5. Miscellaneous Theorems from Other Books of Euclid

THE CIRCLE

49. In the same circle or in equal circles, if two chords are equal, they subtend equal arcs.

50. A line through the center of a circle perpendicular to a chord bisects the chord and the arc subtended by it.

51. In the same circle or in equal circles, equal chords are equidistant from the center and chords equidistant from the center are equal.

52. A line perpendicular to a radius at its extremity is tangent to the circle.

53. The tangents to a circle drawn from an external point are equal and make equal angles with the line joining the point to the center.

54. If two circles are tangent to each other, the line of centers passes through the point of contact.

MEASUREMENT OF ANGLES

55. An inscribed angle is measured by half the intercepted arc.

56. An angle formed by two chords intersecting within the circle is measured by half the sum of the intercepted arcs.

57. An angle formed by a tangent and a chord drawn from the point of contact is measured by half the intercepted arc.

58. An angle formed by two secants, a secant and a tangent, or two tangents drawn to a circle from an external point is measured by half the difference of the intercepted arcs.

PROPORTION AND SIMILAR POLYGONS

Definition

Two polygons are similar if corresponding angles are equal, and corresponding sides proportional.

59. The internal (external) bisector of an angle of a triangle divides the opposite side internally (externally) into segments which are proportional to the adjacent sides, and conversely.

60. If two chords intersect within a circle, the product of the segments of one is equal to the product of the segments of the other.

61. If, from a point outside a circle, a secant and a tangent are drawn, the tangent is the mean proportional between the secant and its external segment.

62. If, in a right triangle, the altitude is drawn upon the hypotenuse,

(a) The two triangles thus formed are similar to the given triangle and to each other.

(b) The altitude is the mean proportional between the segments of the hypotenuse.

(c) Each leg of the given triangle is the mean proportional between the hypotenuse and the segment adjacent to the leg.

63. The perimeters of two similar polygons have the same ratio as any two corresponding sides.

AREAS

64. The area of a parallelogram equals the product of its base by its altitude.

65. The area of a triangle equals half the product of its base by its altitude.

66. The area of a trapezoid is equal to half the product of the sum of its bases by its altitude.

67. The areas of two similar polygons are to each other as the squares on any two corresponding sides.

Appendix B

HILBERT'S AXIOMS

1. Undefined Quantities

A class of undefined elements called *points*, denoted by Latin capitals A, B, C, ...

A class of undefined elements called *lines*, denoted by small Latin letters a, b, c, ...

A class of undefined elements called *planes*, denoted by small Greek letters α, β, γ, ...

Undefined relations: Incidence (being incident, lying on); being in; between; congruence; being parallel; continuous.

2. Axioms of Incidence

Incidence is a symmetric relation between elements of different classes (points, lines, planes) such that

2.1. Given any two points A, B, there exists a line a lying on A and B.

2.2. Given A, B, there exists at most one line a lying on A, B.

2 3. There are at least two points which lie on a given line. There are at least three points which do not lie on a line.

2.4. Whenever A, B, C do not lie on a line, there exists a plane α such that A, B, C lie on α. Given any α, there exists a point lying on α.

2.5. If A, B, C do not lie on a line, there is at most one α lying on A, B, C.

2.6. If two points on a line a lie in a plane α, then every point lying on a is also lying on α.

2.7. If two planes have a point in common, then they have at least one more point in common.

2.8. There are at least four points which do not lie on a plane.

3. Axioms of Order

3.1. If B is between A and C, then A, B, C are three different points on a line and B is between C and A.

3.2. Let A, C be two points and let AC be the line on which A and C lie. Then, there exists at least one point B on AC such that C is between A and B.

3.3. Let A, B, C be points on a line. Then at most one of them is between the two others.

3.4. (*Pasch's Axiom.*) Let A, B, C be three points which are not on a line. Let b be a line in the plane defined by A, B, C such that none of the points A, B, C

lies on b. Let b intersect the line AB in a point D between A and B. Then, there is either a point X or a point Y on b, where X is between A and C and Y is between B and C.

4. Axioms of Congruence

The axioms of incidence and of order make it possible to define the terms "interval," "side of a line or of a plane," "beam or ray," and "angle."

4.1. Let A, B lie on a. Let A' be on a', which may be different from or identical with a. Then it is always possible to find on either side of A' on a' a point B' such that the interval AB is congruent with $A'B'$, i.e., $AB \equiv A'B'$.

4.2. If both $A'B' \equiv AB$ and $A''B'' \equiv AB$, then $A'B' \equiv A''B''$.

4.3. Let AB and BC be two intervals on a which do not have a point in common. Let $A'B'$ and $B'C'$ be two intervals on a' (not necessarily different from a) which also do not have a point in common. Then it follows from

$$AB \equiv A'B' \quad \text{and} \quad BC \equiv B'C'$$
that
$$AC \equiv A'C'$$

4.4. Let (h,k) be an angle between the beams h and k which lie on α. Let a' be in a plane α', and let a side of a' in α' be given. Let h' be a beam on α' which starts from O'. Then there exists in α' exactly one beam k' such that $(h,k) \equiv (h',k')$ and that all inner points of (h',k') lie on the given side of a'. Every angle is congruent to itself.

4.5. If two triangles ABC, $A'B'C'$ satisfy $AB \equiv A'B'$, $AC \equiv A'C'$, $\angle BAC \equiv \angle B'A'C'$, then $\angle ABC \equiv \angle A'B'C'$.

4.5.* In Axiom 4.5, add the restriction that $\angle ABC = \angle A'B'C'$ provided that AB and $A'B'$ define the right-hand beams and that AC and $A'C'$ define the left-hand beams of the angles BAC and $B'A'C'$ respectively. Then, we also have $\angle ACB \equiv \angle A'C'B'$.

5. Axiom of Parallels

Let a be a line, and let A be a point not on a. Let α be the plane determined by a and A. Then there exists precisely one line on α and A which does not intersect a.

6. Axioms of Continuity

6.1. (*Archimedean Axiom.*) If AB and CD are any intervals, then there exist points A_1, A_2, . . . , A_n on the line AB such that

(a) $AA_1 \equiv A_1A_2 \equiv \ldots \equiv A_{n-1}A_n \equiv CD$

(b) B is between A and A_n.

6.1. (*Axiom of Completeness.*) The points on a line form a system which cannot be extended if Axioms 2.1, 2.2, 3.1 to 3.4, 4.1 to 4.,5 and 6.1 remain valid.

6.2.* (*Axiom of Neighborhood.*) If any interval AB is given, then there exists a triangle such that there is no interval congruent to AB in the interior of this triangle.

BIBLIOGRAPHY

1. Altschiller-Court, N.: "College Geometry," Johnson Publishing Co., Richmond, Va., 1923.
2. Baker, Henry F.: "Principles of Geometry," Cambridge University Press, London, 1922.
3. Ballantine, W. B.: "The Logic of Science," Thomas Y. Crowell Company, New York, 1933.
4. Bell, E. T.: "The Search for Truth," The Williams & Wilkins Company, Baltimore, 1937.
5. Bentley, A. F.: "Linguistic Analysis of Mathematics," The Principia Press, Inc., Bloomington, Ind., 1932.
6. Black, Max: "The Nature of Mathematics," Harcourt, Brace and Company, Inc., New York, 1934.
7. Bogoslovsky, Boris B.: "The Technique of Controversy; Principles of Dynamic Logic," Harcourt, Brace and Company, Inc., New York, 1928.
8. Bonola, R.: "Non-Euclidean Geometry," The Open Court Publishing Company, La Salle, Ill., 1912.
9. Busemann, Herbert, and Paul J. Kelly: "Projective Geometry and Projective Matrices," Academic Press, Inc., New York, 1953.
10. Carnap, Rudolf: Foundations of Logic and Mathematics, "International Encyclopedia of Unified Science," vol. 1, no. 3, University of Chicago Press, Chicago, 1939.
11. Carslaw, H. S.: "The Elements of Non-Euclidean Geometry," Longmans, Green & Co., Inc., New York, 1916.
12. Christofferson, H. D.: "Geometry Professionalized," George Banta Publishing Company, (The Collegiate Press), Menasha, Wis., 1933.
13. Cohen, M., and E. Nagel: "Introduction to Logic and the Scientific Method," Harcourt, Brace and Company, Inc., New York, 1934.
14. Columbia Associates of Philosophy: "Introduction to Reflective Thinking," Houghton Mifflin and Company, Boston, 1923.
15. Cooley, H. R., D. Gans, M. Kline, and H. Wahlert: "Introduction to Mathematics," Houghton Mifflin Company, Boston, 1949.
16. ———, P. H. Graham, F. W. John, and A. Tilley: "College Algebra," McGraw-Hill Book Company, Inc., New York, 1942.
17. Courant, R., and H. Robbins: "What Is Mathematics?" Oxford University Press, New York, 1941.
18. Coxeter, H. S. M.: "The Real Projective Plane," McGraw-Hill Book Company, Inc., New York, 1949.

19. ———: "Non-Euclidean Geometry," University of Toronto Press, Toronto, 1947.
20. Daus, Paul: "College Geometry," Prentice-Hall, Inc., New York, 1941.
21. Davis, David R.: "Modern College Geometry," Addison-Wesley Publishing Company, Cambridge, Mass., 1949.
22. Dresden, A.: "An Invitation to Mathematics," Henry Holt and Company, Inc., New York, 1936.
23. Eddington, Sir Arthur S.: "Space, Time and Gravitation," Cambridge University Press, London, 1920.
24. ———: "The Nature of the Physical World," The Macmillan Company, New York, 1928.
25. Enriques, F.: "The Historic Development of Logic," translated by J. Rosenthal, Henry Holt and Company, Inc., New York, 1929.
26. Faulkner, T. E.: "Projective Geometry," 2d ed., Interscience Publishers, Inc., New York, 1952.
27. Forder, H. G.: "The Foundations of Euclidean Geometry," Cambridge University Press, London, 1927.
28. Graustein, W. E.: "Introduction to Higher Geometry," The Macmillan Company, New York, 1945.
29. Heath, T. L.: "The Thirteen Books of Euclid's Elements," Cambridge University Press, New York, 1926.
30. Hilbert, D.: "The Foundations of Geometry," 6th and 7th eds., The Open Court Publishing Company, La Salle, Ill., 1938.
31. ——— and S. Cohn-Vossen: "Geometry and the Imagination," Chelsea Publishing Co., New York, 1952.
32. Holgate, T. F.: "Projective Geometry," The Macmillan Company, New York, 1930.
33. Johnson, R. A.: "Modern Geometry," Houghton Mifflin Company, Boston, 1929.
34. Jones, Burton Q.: "Elementary Concepts of Mathematics," The Macmillan Company, New York, 1947.
35. Kempe, A. B.: "How to Draw a Straight Line," Macmillan & Co., Ltd., London, 1877.
36. Keyser, C. J.: "Human Worth of Rigorous Thinking," Columbia University Press, New York, 1925.
37. Klein, Felix: "Elementary Geometry from an Advanced Standpoint," The Macmillan Company, New York, 1932.
38. Kline, Morris: "Mathematics in Western Culture," Oxford University Press, New York, 1953.
39. Korzybski, Alfred: "Science and Sanity," 3d ed., The International Non-Aristotelian Library Publishing Co., Lakeville, Conn., 1948.
40. Lehmer, D. N.: "An Elementary Course in Synthetic Projective Geometry," Ginn & Company, Boston, 1917.
41. Lieber, Hugh G., and Lillian R. Lieber: "Non-Euclidean Geometry," Academy Press, New York, 1931.
42. Luneberg, Rudolph K.: "Mathematical Analysis of Binocular Vision," Princeton University Press, Princeton, N. J., 1947.
43. MacNeish, H. F.: Four Finite Geometries, *American Mathematical Monthly*, vol. XLIX, pp. 15–23, 1942.
44. Manning, Henry P.: "Non-Euclidean Geometry," Ginn & Company, Boston, 1901.

45. Meserve, B. E.: "Fundamental Concepts of Geometry," Addison-Wesley Publishing Company, Cambridge, Mass., 1955.

46. O'Hara, C. W., and D. R. Ward: "An Introduction to Projective Geometry," Oxford University Press, New York, 1937.

47. Poincaré, H.: "The Foundations of Science," The Science Press, New York, 1913.

48. ———: "Science and Hypothesis," translated by G. B. Halsted, The Science Press, New York, 1905; also Dover Publications, New York, 1952.

49. ———: "Science and Method," translated by G. B. Halsted, The Science Press, New York, 1913.

50. Quine, W. W.: "Methods of Logic," Henry Holt and Company, Inc., New York, 1950.

51. Ramsey, F. P.: "The Foundations of Mathematics," Kegan Paul, Trench, Trubner & Co., London, 1931.

52. Robinson, G. de B.: "The Foundations of Geometry," University of Toronto Press, Toronto, 1940.

53. Ruskin, John: "The Elements of Drawing and Perspective," John Wiley & Sons, Inc., New York, 1885.

54. Russell, Bertrand: "Introduction to Mathematical Philosophy," George Allen & Unwin, Ltd., London, 1919.

55. ———: "The Foundations of Geometry," Cambridge University Press, London, 1897.

56. ———: "Mysticism and Logic and Other Essays," Longmans, Green & Co., Ltd., London, 1917.

57. ———: "Our Knowledge of the External World," George Allen & Unwin, Ltd., London, 1926.

58. Sanger, R. G.: "Synthetic Projective Geometry," McGraw-Hill Book Company, Inc., New York, 1939.

59. Shively, L. S.: "Modern Geometry," John Wiley & Sons, Inc., New York, 1939.

60. Smith, D. E., George Wentworth: "Plane and Solid Geometry," Ginn & Company, Boston, 1913.

61. Smith, P. A. Gale, and J. Neeley: "New Analytic Geometry," Ginn & Company, Boston, 1928.

62. Stabler, E. R.: "An Introduction to Mathematical Thought," Addison-Wesley Publishing Company, Cambridge, Mass., 1953.

63. ———: An Interpretation and Comparison of Three Schools of Thought in the Foundations of Mathematics, *The Mathematics Teacher*, vol. 28, pp. 5–35, 1935.

64. Struik, Dirk J.: "Lectures on Analytic and Projective Geometry," Addison-Wesley Publishing Company, Cambridge, Mass., 1953.

65. Tarski, A.: "An Introduction to Logic," Oxford University Press, New York, 1939.

66. Taylor, E. H., and G. C. Bartoo: "An Introduction to College Geometry," The Macmillan Company, New York, 1949.

67. Veblen, O., and J. W. Young: "Projective Geometry," vols. I and II, Ginn & Company, Boston, 1910.

68. Watson, Emery Ernest: "Elements of Projective Geometry," D. C. Heath and Company, Boston, 1935.

69. Weyl, Herman: "Philosophy of Mathematics and Natural Sciences," Princeton University Press, Princeton, N. J., 1949.

70. ————: Mathematics and Logic, *American Mathematical Monthly*, vol. 35, pp. 2–13, 1946.

71. Whitehead, A. N.: "An Introduction to Mathematics," Henry Holt and Company, Inc., New York, 1911.

72. Wilder, R. L.: "Introduction to the Foundations of Mathematics," John Wiley & Sons, Inc., New York, 1952.

73. Winger, R. M.: "An Introduction to Projective Geometry," D. C. Heath and Company, Boston, 1923.

74. Wolfe, H. E.: "Introduction to Non-Euclidean Geometry," The Dryden Press, Inc., New York, 1945.

75. Young, J. W.: "Lectures on Fundamental Concepts of Algebra and Geometry," The Macmillan Company, New York, 1925.

76. Young, J. W.: "Projective Geometry," Carus Monographs, The Open Court Publishing Company, La Salle, Ill., 1930.

77. Young, J. W. A.: "Monographs on Topics of Modern Mathematics," Dover Publications, Inc., New York, 1955.

INDEX